*March of America Facsimile Series*

*Number 68*

# New Homes in the West

Catherine Stewart

# New Homes
# in the West

*by Catherine Stewart*

**ANN ARBOR**

**UNIVERSITY MICROFILMS, INC.**

*A Subsidiary of Xerox Corporation*

# Foreword

Reactions to the West were as varied as the people who experienced it. For some the West was the scene of disappointment and personal tragedy; for others it was a place of opportunity and promise. *New Homes in the West*, written by Catherine Stewart and published in 1843, is an extreme example of the latter point of view. Almost everything the author had observed in over a decade of travel in the Midwest filled her with overpowering enthusiasm. Although she acknowledged that "those who have never witnessed the picturesque scenery described" might object "that an ideal beauty is thrown around it," yet she continued in unrestrained praise of the West.

Many of the author's prose commentaries are in the form of letters addressed to a friend in Buffalo, New York. Most concern the Michigan and Illinois country, although some are given over to descriptions of Tennessee and Missouri.

It was not just the great natural beauty of the Midwestern country which so excited Catherine Stewart. She also saw the region as an asylum for the poor and the oppressed, "where want need not be known; where despair need not cloud the mind; where life may feel a new impulse." As she surveyed the western territory her conviction grew that the time was not far distant "when the deep solitudes of the trackless wastes spread far away, will be enlivened with the hum of busy enterprise, and covered over with a hardy, industrious population."

The author wrote with affection about the Indians whom she had encountered, and she described with avid interest their folkways. Although the tide of western emigration was now pushing them out of these territories, she believed that perhaps it was all for the best. "Since the policy of our government has rendered their removal necessary, it is pleasant to think they are happier in situations that open new and wider fields for their favorite pursuits." The same optimism colored her judgment of southern slave territory. She agreed that universal emancipation was to be desired. Still, "many pictures might be drawn of the comfortable condition of the well fed, well clothed, merry negroes at the south." Often, she thought, the slaves were at least as happy as their masters.

The several poetical offerings which Catherine Stewart appended to her book sounded many of the same themes.

"O come to the lovely, luxuriant west!
  Come recline with me under my bower;
  Where the redbreast sings, and the dove
      builds her nest,
  In this land of the shade, and the flower."

If the language is rather too saccharine for modern taste, the author's admiration for the West is evident.

Little is known about the author other than what may be gleaned from allusions in her book. To situate *New Homes in the West* in the context of other contemporaneous writing, see Ralph Leslie Rusk, *The Literature of the Middle Western Frontier* (New York, 1962), I, 79-130.

# NEW HOMES

## IN

# THE WEST.

BY

CATHERINE STEWART.

---

"When thy star of destiny declineth, seek a new influence
in some distant region."

---

NASHVILLE.

CAMERON AND FALL, DEADERICK STREET.

M DCCC XLIII.

# INTRODUCTION

When the Prairies of the West first open to the view, in all their vastness, and all their beauty of flowers, and light oak openings; with lakes innumerable, that brightly mirror earth and sky; the mind seems under some magic influence; and is only half disenchanted of its spell, when the view of a humble cottage nestling under the greenwood side, unfolds the reality of a peaceful seclusion, far away from the cares and illusions of the busy world.

An onward course over the Far West, disclosing new and varied claims to admiration, created a wish that other travellers might be persuaded to visit regions so highly interesting; and impelled the writer of the following pages to sketch a few brief outlines, and to hazard the daring experiment of submitting them to the public eye.

She is aware that criticism may seize upon the idea, very natural to those who have never witnessed the picturesque scenery described, that an ideal beauty is thrown around it. If the views seem too vivid and rare, she, perhaps may be allowed to claim this as an evidence that she has, in some measure, succeeded in doing justice to that which bids defiance to description.

On reviewing her work, she has her fears lest she may have strown her path too profusely with flowers; and has even lopped off many a lily and violet; and with a sigh, has seen them drop away, one by one; but where these things are forever springing up, with their bright influences, it is but grateful to give them a passing notice; and she hopes that the offering here made, will not be the less acceptable, that it is wreathed with the cheering emblems of Hope.

To those who awake from the pleasing dream of happiness and security, to the stern reality of a frowning fortune, she would point out asylums of peace and beauty; and invite them to repair, where nature seems waiting to open her stores of rich abundance; to form new hopes, new associations, and new homes.

# NEW HOMES IN THE WEST.

"We will rear new homes under trees that glow,
As if gems were the fruitage of every bough;
O'er our white walls we will train the vine
And sit in its shadow at day's decline;
And watch our herds as they range at will,
Through the green savannas, all bright and still."

*Song of Emigration.*

In the summer of 1830, the beautiful regions of the West, first called forth the lively admiration, which far from diminishing, has only increased by an onward pilgrimage over that spirit-stirring new world.

Until within a few years previous to this period, the southern part of the Territory of Michigan had been almost entirely unexplored by the white man; and with the

1*

exception of a few scattered settlements, un-
redeemed from the wild empire of nature.

The French, those early wanderers over
the western frontiers, more than a century
ago, traversed the shores of lakes St. Clair,
Huron and Michigan; and with their innate
taste for the picturesque, settled along the
margins of the bold water-courses that fertilize those regions, seldom penetrating the
interior of the peninsula; contented, in the
simplicity of their habits, with very limited
improvements; a garden and fruit trees being almost the boundary of their views.

Emigration has now, happily, received an
impetus, and its course is onward, over this
fertile reservation of country, unchecked
even by the waters of the Mississippi.

The traveller, impelled by glowing descriptions of the west, must inevitably feel
disappointment during the first day's journey from Detroit; the low, marshy wilderness

presenting only a repulsive aspect, until he
enters the country watered by St. Joseph's
river, which winds beautifully, through flowery prairies, and groves of dense luxuriance; whose branches are often bending under the weight of fruitful vines.

Riding through this section of country,
one is led to admire the power of intuition,
or rather the close observation of the Indian, when viewing the trail along side of
the road, which served as a guide to the
commissioners in laying it off, a distance of
300 miles from Detroit to Chicago. These
trails were made by the Sauk and Fox Indians, on their journeyings to Malden, where
they were lured for many years, by annual
presents or bribes from the English.

Another chronicle of this strange race is
to be seen on this route. Not far from the
road, is a rock of a conical form, held in
devout veneration, that has many indenta-

tions which tradition says are impressions of the footsteps of a spirit which, at times, formerly came from on high, and stood there. On this rock, the passing child of the forest leaves his offering of tobacco; and there, is always to be seen, a portion of this *fragrant* incense.

Among the new villages springing up, is White Pigeon, or Wa-bish-ke-pe-nah, a-bout 150 miles from Detroit; deriving its name from an Indian Chief. It stands on an extensive prairie which, for miles around, presents such attractions as to have rivetted many English farmers to the spot, who with their well known taste and skill, have imparted to the land the aspect of a highly cultivated country. Many of them have planted quickset hedges for enclosures to their grounds. Rich pasturage being an original feature of the land, they have already established very extensive dairies.

The soil is not only adapted to all kinds of grain, but here, as in many other places, combines with a climate suited to the culture of the grape and morus multicaulis; and the time may not be far distant, when smiling vintages, and the manufacture of silk, will become sources of affluence to this overflowing land.

St. Joseph river, after winding through a wide extent of country, flows boldly past the flourishing village of Niles, and empties into lake Michigan, twenty miles distant. In 1826, only a few log cabins marked this spot, erected by several enterprising spirits, who then laid the foundation of their present prosperity. Near this place, are several fine large mills and the fertile adjacent country is fast filling up.

There are still remaining, many traces of the French, who, in bygone days, roamed along the margin of St. Joseph river.

A rude cross stands at the head of a grave, supposed to be a memorial of one of their missionaries. Further on, the ruins of an ancient fort, add another to the many mysteries here, that shut out all light from the enquiring mind.

The imagination floats pleasantly over the future destiny of this new world. The eastern states have already poured in countless numbers of farmers and mechanics; and exiles from Europe furnish many tributary streams to swell the mighty current. Were it more generally known, how small a capital would serve for a settlement in its incipiency, it would, doubtless, add to the immense list of immigrants, pressing on to fill up these waste lands. A man, with the little gatherings of his industry, may repair, where land of the first quality is sold for one dollar and twenty-five cents an acre; three yoke of oxen are required to break up the soil, which at first, is stubborn; these, together with plough, harrow, wagon and other farming implements, will not exceed three hundred dollars. A comfortable log cabin may be made with a trifling expense; the groves of timber serve for fencing and fuel. Thus with six hundred dollars at farthest, the honest, industrious adventurer may, with moderate wishes, lay the sure foundation of a comfortable independence. A large family is no incumbrance. The little hive will constitute a part of his wealth. The bands of sturdy yeomanry in embryo, swarming in the steerage of steamers on the northern lakes, promise, in time, to become the most valuable portion of the American community; forming a part of the sovereign people; and contributing to the "wordy contest" of presidential elections.

The pre-emption law, that happy feature in our government; that boon to the poor

man; enables him, if he so wishes, to enter a tract of land sufficient for a farm, without an immediate advance; when it comes
in market, with the avails of his industry,
he may pay for his claim, and go forth, unimpeded, in his praiseworthy enterprise.

To such as are deterred from fear of ague
and fever, it might be observed, that those
who avoid locating near a watercourse, and
use proper precaution, usually escape those
scourges of the new settler.

The population is becoming, every year,
more interesting in its material. To the
mutability of fortune, these borders are indebted for the intellectual tone of character, which is giving elevation to society;
and placing it on a grade of refinement,
equal to the most *recherche* circles of eastern cities.   One frequently feels agreeable
surprise, on entering a cabin of simplest
structure, to find all that winning hospitali-

ty and intelligence that grace the fashiona-
ble saloons; more appreciated, in their humble garb, than when surrounded with osten-
tatious display.

The wrecked in fortune, whether from
having ventured too far on the wild stream
of speculation, or from imposition on honest credulity; baffled in his purposes at
home, may gather up his shattered remnants,
and is soon felicitating himself that he is in
a quiet harbor, where he may securely steer
his light barque under the willows. The
depressed with "all the various ills that flesh
is heir to," may here find a sanctuary, whose
Sabbath loveliness will, once more, reconcile
him to life. As his leisure or taste may di-
rect, he may draw delicious fish from the
lakes, or pursue the bounding deer along
their flowery margins—He may find his heart
warmed into philanthropy, though he may

2

have believed it could never again throb
with the pulse of hope or joy.

The brightest picture must have its dark
shades.   Vice and degradation are diffused
through every society; and it is well that
a man should be armed at all points, to turn
aside the arts of the wily and selfish, who
always contribute to the heterogeneous mass
of a new community.   Borne on by a restless desire of change these settlers, frequently separate before they have lived together long enough to become united in the
enduring bonds of fellowship.  It is too true,
that moral obligation in many cases, sits too
lightly; the natural consequence of infidel-
ity, which ever prevails where the light of
the Gospel is withheld, or but partially administered.  The desecration of the Sabbath,
in many places, calls aloud to the dispensers
of religious instruction, to rise up, with divine
revelation in their hands, and come away.

LETTER TO MRS. B*****, BUFFALO, N. Y.

### St. Joseph, Mich., 1832.

I WRITE you from an Indian reservation, where circumstances, peculiar in their nature, have made me, for an indefinite period, a sojourner; and thrown me in a situation novel and altogether *unique*. Satiety of the world's rich banquetings may, in some cases, prepare us to relish the rigid simplicity of natural fare; but whether an atmosphere of intellectual life can be exchanged without a sigh of regret, for even an empire over a savage community, remains to be tested. The Indians call me coma-queh, their word for queen, but I shall willingly lay aside my title of royalty, to mingle with the friends who may occasionally penetrate these sequestered recesses.

Here, with lakes and forests intervening

between us and the busy world, books and
papers come as cheerful messengers, opening a pleasing avenue to social life; bringing, as it were, the universal globe, with its
prominent actors, to our door, with a rigid
truth of coloring, less faithful perhaps in
their impressions on minds under their immediate influences.

Picture to yourself, a rude cabin on a
gentle elevation, shaded with large forest
trees, the resort of singing birds; a clear
spring gushing from a rock overhung by a
wide spreading oak. The airs must be salubrious which come freighted with the odor
of flowers from the prairies. Mats made
by Indian women, dyed with plants that
produce bright and lasting colors, supply the
place of carpets; and mantel ornaments of
the branching antlers of the deer, discourse
of the chase and the surrounding population; who bring me venison and wild fruits.

An Indian girl, partially educated by Missionaries, has found her way to my heart, and is ever by my side, except when occasionally her propensity for the woods induces her to stray away.  Her name is Wa-wa-smo-queh, or lightning woman; every way expressive of her movements.

The timid fear with which I at first shrunk from these strange people, has subsided, and a mutual confidence exists.  I freely give them my hand; and have made myself sufficiently familiar with their language, to converse with them.  It is pleasant to witness their gratified looks when I seat myself on a mat within their wigwams. So noiseless is their step, I sometimes start with surprise on finding them looking in at my window, while engaged in sewing or reading.  The word buk-a-tah, (hungry) they know is an appeal irresistible; and always call forth some of those little attentions most gratifying to them.

I feel a deep interest in these children of the forest; and study their manners and propensities with minute investigation. It is refreshing to drink from such transparent fountains. Indeed, there is much spread out before me, to induce an epicurism of the mind. Divested of the foreign drapery of education, like fine statuary, they are presented to the contemplation, in all the unconfined, easy lines of nature. Living however, as they do, on the borders of civilization, some of the vices of the white man are engrafted on the natural stock. Selfishness is a predominant passion with them; though their sagacity may have led them to perceive, that to meet mankind on their own ground, they must adopt the weapons of self-defence. In many instances, their credulous natures have made them dupes of the wily Indian trader, who enriches himself from the proceeds of their annuities received from government. To that source, may be attributed many of the irregularities, which an unrestrained use of their "fire water" has produced. When unintoxicated, or unprovoked, this tribe is quiet and unoffending. Indolence characterises the men, though their youths display great agility; seldom unaccompanied with the bow and arrow, and fleet as the deer himself. The women are unremitting in their industry; they make their houses of bark; cultivate and gather in their corn; make baskets and moccasins for sale; and sugar, in large quantities; for which purpose, they annually migrate to their maple groves. The men kill the deer, and their patient endurance of fatigue, and privations from cold and hunger is incredible. The women dress the skins of their game, while their lords lie at ease, under the shade, playing at cards or other games of chance; often engaged in athletic amusements.

Wrapped in serious gravity or proud taciturnity, their real characters are shut in from the view of the white man; but to one who may have chanced to witness their gaming circles, the animated countenance and loud laugh, show that they can unbend, like our own votaries of pleasure. When reclining in their favorite haunts, in all their tinsel finery, they form the most grotesque groups. They have an innate fondness for baubles; wear large, gay shawls twisted round their heads, much in the Turkish style; sometimes, with a feather; their ornaments always disposed for effect; if only a branch of leaves, it is set as a plume, or worn as a wreath round their unintelligent brows. Paint is an indispensable accompaniment of their toilet. The Indian bears along with him, his tiny looking glass; and often under a tree, stops to repair this finish to his attractions. He is bold, easy, and often graceful in his attitudes. His walk reminds me of our distinguished tragedians as they tread the stage. Like them he firmly plants the foot, and draws his mantle in folds about him, with the same commanding air of deportment, with this difference, his regal dignity is natural, while theirs is only assumed. He could not have studied them; and it is not probable they have taken a Pottawattamie Indian as their model.

It is to be regretted that all efforts have as yet been but partially successful to civilize this benighted race. With minds as susceptible of cultivation as their waste prairies, the light imparted merely tinges the dark surface, to be dispelled when their loved hunting grounds lure them away to assume again, the blanket and tomahawk.

## MISSIONARIES.

"Yet shall the gloom which wraps thy hills be broken,
And the full day-spring rise upon thy race!
And fading mists the better paths disclose,
And the wild desert blossom as the rose."

THE place called Carey Mission, after-
wards converted into an Indian agency,
lies near St. Joseph river, on that beautiful
and very desirable tract of land ten miles
square, which once formed an Indian reservation.

There, some years ago, a band of Missionaries was established by the Baptist
Board of Missions, at Boston, for the purpose of educating on christian principles,
the rising generation of Indians. An institution consisting of nearly a hundred
pupils, flourished for a few years, when it
began to languish, and was finally abandoned. At the treaty of 1828, the buildings

were sold to government. A few young
Indians were transferred to schools in New
York; the others, with scarcely an exception, are left to roam at will, and have re-
lapsed into the idleness and vagrancy of un-
civilized life.

A few years later, a French Roman Catholic Priest was stationed at the village of an
Indian Chief on the same reservation. This
man of profound erudition, with untiring
zeal and exertion, drew around him a large
number of Indian children, and with a pious auxiliary, a nun seventy years of age,
under flattering auspices, and the salutary
restraint that confession of sins imposes,
was making happy advances in civilizing
many of all ages. The nun, fervently de-
voted to the cause, familiar with their language and habits, seemed moulding anew
their natures. She daily dispensed religious
instructions, and interpreted those of the

holy father. They seemed in their philanthropy to deem it no sacrifice to abandon congenial society, and bury themselves in the wilderness, suffering many privations, living on the simplest fare, and sleeping on pallets of straw. Thus associated, and under circumstances so peculiar, the ceremony of baptism administered to some of their young converts, presented a scene, which is still vivid on the memory.

An altar raised in a small cabin must be simple, if not rude, in structure. Such was that before which the priest kneeled in his sacerdotal robes, with emblematic paintings; the chalice and the cross; the wine and the wafer; all intended for the effect doubtless produced on the savage mind.

The subjects for baptism, with white napkins thrown over their heads, kneeled down, and after the sacred rites were performed, and all had together prayed, and chanted

in Latin, the priest addressed them in
French, which was interpreted to them by
the nun; her very remarkable features shaded by a cap, tied with a black ribbon. Her
voice and gestures were gentle and persua-
sive, at times vehement; enlisting a solemn
and hushed attention. At the close of the
service, Po-ke-gan, the Chief of the village,
addressed this Pottawattamie congregation
out of doors. His earnest solicitude; his
benevolent aspect; the wind blowing through
his gray hairs; altogether, formed a spectacle of deep interest.

To witness an Indian wigwam serving
for a Papal Chapel, the savage crossing
himself and kneeling before the altar in solemn devotion; the conviction forces itself
on the mind, that the different forms of the
laborer are not material; if he plants good
seed and waters the growth, it will meet the
smiles of Deity.

A melancholy occurrence which took place soon after, furnishes another instance of the sway this man held over the Indians. At a wabina or festive dance, under the influence of the dark passions, jealousy and revenge, heightened by intoxication, one of their Chiefs attacked To-pin-i-be, the principal Chief of the nation, who stabbed him to the heart with a dirk, the inseparable accompaniment of the wampum belt. Early on the following morning, the Chief repaired to the residence of their agent, and asked him if he was going to have him hanged for the offence. The affair was laid before the civil authority, who declined any interference. The day after the interment, the brother of the deceased stated to the agent, that they had buried him before the house of To-pin-i-be, which signified, in accordance with their customs, that life for life was demanded. The young Chief was

found at his wigwam, eating boiled hominy
with his wife and children, entirely composed; aware at the same time of his im-
pending fate, unless some compromise could
be made to induce the relations to "take the
body;" a prospect of which was almost
hopeless. He offered to give all he possessed, for so desirable a termination of the
affair. "Not," said he, "that I fear to die,
but our laws requiring life for life, will em-
broil the relations in a long warfare, and I
would gladly spare so much bloodshed."

The brother, in the meantime, repaired
to the distant abode of one of their prophets,
and returned with a slip of wood on which
a prophecy was carved. At the top was a
representation of beautiful hunting grounds,
the future paradise of the Indians; at the
bottom, was brought out to view, the place of
torment, where the Chief was, and would
remain, were not the law carried into effect.

A solemn council was then convened of about a hundred on each side; consisting of the relatives and the grave and wise of the nation. A number of horses were standing in view, packed with large quantities of goods; portions of their annual payments brought by the friends of To-pin-i-be; which, with his own property, were tendered for the purchase of his life. To this august assembly, Po-ke-gan made a speech, in which all his powers of oratory seemed called forth on this momentous subject of life and death. The Roman Catholic Priest then rose, and threw his weight in the scale. In the varying expressions of the faces turned towards him, might be traced the effect of his arguments, in chasing away the mists that hung over their superstitious minds. A silence of some length ensued. In the meantime, the culprit Chief was lying a short distance apart under a shade, awaiting with calm composure the result of the council. Whether the alluring packages in view lent a charm or not, to the force of the holy father's eloquence, the affair thus eventuated. After a low and protracted consultation among the aggrieved party, the brother came out from among them, and stepping forward, proclaimed that they would "*take the body.*" The meeting hereupon dispersed. The Indian was immediately disinterred, and together with the offerings, was carried away and buried with his friends.

3*

## AN INDIAN COUNCIL.

"A lofty place where leader sat
Around the council board
In festive halls, a chair of state,
When the blood-red wine was pour'd,
A name that drew a prouder tone,
From herald, harp and bard—
Surely these things were all thine own
So hadst thou thy reward."

SOME years ago, a council was held in
Michigan, on the St. Joseph river, between
Gen. Grover, Indian agent, and Judge Polk
of Indiana, on the part of the United States,
and the principal Chiefs of the Pottawattamie nation, on that of the Indians; the pro-
fessed object of which, was to have a full
understanding of the letter and meaning of
the treaty of the Wabash, held in 1828.
The United States claimed by this treaty,
the cession by the Pottawattamies to the
State of Indiana, of one section of land for
every mile of a road to be made by that

State from the head of lake Michigan to the Ohio river; besides sufficient ground for the road as far as it should extend through their lands.

The *coup d' oeil* of these lords of the land, about one hundred in number, convened on a green knoll in all the "pomp and circumstance" of Indian costume, presented a spectacle truly imposing. The principal Chiefs sat in front, while others were lying around in various directions. In their easy self-possession and calm gravity, they formed an assemblage which, in dignity at least, might have compared with some of our own legislative councils. Their recumbent attitudes served to bring up in the mind of the observer, associations with the ancient philosophers, had not their tinsel decorations and gaudy colors presented so much of the grotesque as to banish the idea, and cause a smile of pity to blend itself with admiration. Silver rings dangled from their noses and ears, while flowers from the prairies plumed the turbans of the young and thoughtless. Some of their faces were painted red, others black; this color always prevailing when they are under the influence of dark passions. The young Chief was there in his court dress, a scarlet broad cloth mantle, with three long black feathers waving over his back. A silver medal bearing the head of Gen. Jackson, was suspended from his neck; broad bands of the same on his arms. This Chief of the nation, though modest and unassuming, is, from his rank, always a distinguished personage in their conventions of whatever kind.

Po-ke-gan, the orator, was the prominent figure in the fore ground. Intense feeling was visible in every lineament of his face. In his eye, anxiety and deep thought were blended, and around his mouth, care was traced in deep furrows. He sat with his back braced against the stump of a hickory tree; accident thus placing him in a situation, than which no other could have been selected to have expressed more emphatically the nature and condition of his race. This pliant tree of the forest will long bend ere it is broken: yet it may be cut down in its vigor, and the verdant glory of its leaf.

The council was opened through an interpreter, by Gen. Grover, who rose and said. "My red brethren, we come here, by order of your great father, the President of the United States. The treaty of Wabash bears the signature of the Chiefs here assembled, to the grant of a section of land for every mile of a road laid off through your nation, to defray the expense of such road. We come prepared for the survey of the land."

Po-ke-gan, without rising, spoke as follows: "My white brothers—I talk in the name of this nation; we are glad to see you, and bid you welcome, if you come as friends. The Great Spirit looks down upon us. He knows the truth."

He then went on to say, that there was a misunderstanding. That as they understood the articles of the treaty, at the time it was read to them, they had merely ceded as much of their lands as the contemplated road would cover; but the grant of a section for every mile of said road, was what they had never thought of. He then in a decided manner, put in his negative; adding, "if my words do not satisfy you, let all these Chiefs answer for themselves. Let them speak." This application was followed by a unanimous confirmation by the signers of the treaty of the impression entertained by them. The representatives of the United States then had recourse to mild reasoning,

to persuade the Indians that resistance
should not be persisted in; telling them the
mere circumstance of surveying their ground
did not lessen their claim. They remained inflexible. It was thereupon stated, that
they had hoped their red brothers would
have amicably, and in good faith, fulfilled
the obligation held forth in the paper bearing their names; that as far as they were
concerned, they were in duty bound to
coerce an observance of the treaty. Me-
naces were then resorted to, with a view to
intimidate and bring them to submission.

Loud and angry words then ensued, and
a murmur of discontent moved through the
multitude like the heaving of tumultuous
waves; when at length, Po-ke-gan rose
from his seat and thus spoke: "I protest
against your proceeding in this business. Is
it not enough, that we give you our land for
your high-way through our nation? Am I

a child, that you persuade me, that I and my
brothers should say one thing, and do another? You have heard them say that it
was not their meaning to pay the expenses
of your road. We heed not your threats."

Gen. Grover then observed, "our red brethren are in no good humor to-day. They
perhaps are getting hungry. We will ad-
journ and meet again to-morrow, when they
shall have plenty of beef; that will perhaps
make them more favorably disposed."

They moodily declined, saying they were
not buk-a-tah (hungry) for the white man's
bread and meat.

The representatives upon this, rose and
said the survey would be made; that the Indians might cut the chain if they would, as
they had threatened to do. "We will see."

Po-ke-gan, with fiery indignation flashing from his dark eye, while every muscle
of his honest face was in motion, advanced

very near to the agent residing among them, and placing his hand on the breast of the latter exclaimed, "you told us you came here to be our Father; that you were sent here by our Great Father the President, to protect us from wrong; now shew us that your words are not air; that you are our Father." With evident emotion, he replied, "Po-ke-gan, here is my hand. I am your friend, and as such, advise you by no means to cut the surveyor's chain. It will avail you nothing. You can enter your protest, and thus leave room for re-consideration. I see no other course for you."

The intense feeling depicted on the faces of these original landholders, would have furnished a fine subject for the pencil; it was a painful one to witness. Their lofty natures seemed struggling for a few moments with a conviction of their destiny; trembling with deep agitation, which at

4

length subsided into a subdued and mortified expression.

The council adjourned. The poor, browbeat Chiefs of a nation, with all the other Indians, separated; the youth galloping carelessly off on their ponies; the old and thoughtful, gathering their blankets arouud them, moved slowly away to their wigwams, doubtless feeling that their independence existed only in the name. The survey was made. A protest was entered; the result is well known.

At the treaty of Chicago in 1833, the Pottawattamies relinquished their title to all their lands. Previous to their setting out for that place, a friend in an interview with one of the Chiefs, asked him if it was their intention to go beyond the Mississippi. His reply was, "Cho, Saukee akimbo Pottawattamie." "No, the Sacs will kill the Pottawattamies."

The smoke has long since ceased to a-
rise from their lodges; they have turned a
last, lingering look on their beautiful reservation, and on the graves of their fathers,
on the St. Joseph river, and are now roam-
ing over their new hunting grounds, beyond
the Mississippi.

## MEDICINE DANCE.

"Fount of the Chapel with ages grey!
Thou art springing freshly amidst decay.
Thy rites are closed and thy cross lies low,
And the changeful hours breathe o'er thee now.
Yet if at thine altar one holy thought
In man's deep spirit of old hath wrought,
If peace to the mourner, hath here been given,
Or prayer from a chastened heart to heaven,
Be the spot still hallowed while time shall reign."

OF all the religious observances over-
shadowed by superstition, a Medicine
Dance, or Me-ta-me-go-sha of the Pottawattamies, is perhaps the most strange, and
not altogether divested of the ludicrous.
To witness this extraordinary ceremony, a
party, in times past, set out, and surmount-
ing many difficulties in passing through a
dense forest, and finally crossing a stream
of water on a fallen tree, arrived after dark
at the scene of mystic revelling.

Near one of the wigwams of the village,

kettles of venison were suspended from
poles, over a large fire.   Around this festive preparation, groups of Indians were sitting, while others were standing, or moving
to and fro.   The boiling of the kettles
brought to mind the oft repeated

> "Double double toil and trouble
> Fire burn and caldron bubble."

But those beings, with their fantastic cos-
tumes, and dark, scrutinizing eyes, were calculated to create sensations in persons un-
used to them, less comfortable than the idea
of little fairies or witches.   An Indian woman handing a basket of wild plums to her
white visitors, in a measure reassured them,
and they forthwith regaled themselves, seated on mats around the fire.

Presently the drum beat, and raising a
piece of bark, which served as a door, they
entered a wigwam, where as yet only three
persons were assembled.   Ne-se-wa-be, the

4*

grand high priest, or medicine man, old and attenuated, presided over the ceremonies. He rehearsed some strange jargon, with much fluency, not wholly intelligible to the interpreter; it however, had an allusion to the creation of the world, and events handed down by tradition. He was sitting on a mat with two others, who beat a drum composed of some rude material, and rattled a gourd filled with deer's teeth. With a solemn gravity of mien, their eyes fastened on the ground, they seemed totally absorbed in the solemnity of the occasion.

After some time passed in this way, others having arrived and seated themselves round the fire in the middle of the wigwam; they all rose, men and women, and began to dance with much moderation, to the music of the drum and gourd, never raising their feet, except the heel a little, their heads bending down as if in serious reflection.

Old Ne-se-wa-be displayed more agility than any one else; his adroitness evincing that he was no novice in these ancient mysterious rites. They moved, one after the other, round the fire, some of them holding the skin of a small white animal which they kept in a horizontal position, with the head foremost. When in this way, it was pointed towards any one outside of the circle, he fell immediately to the ground, all animation apparently suspended.

Whether these rites were performed on the initiation of a new member, or for the restoration of a sick person, was not fully comprehended by the spectators; who finding them too monotonous, and feeling no disposition. if permitted, to participate in the festive termination of the dance, departed. This is deferred till near daylight, when the venison being steeped into a savory broth, the dancers refresh themselves at the caldrons, and take away the meat to be eaten at their homes on the following day.

Another instance of the superstitious credulity of that nation occurred about the same period. An Indian girl partially educated, came to the writer, with the strange information that the wife of one of the Chiefs had been dead all night, but was alive. Hastening to the spot, the scene here described, presented itself.

## "THE RULING PASSION STRONG IN DEATH."

"White woman! come with me; I've heard thee say,
Thou lovest to trace the footsteps strange and wild,
That nature on the minds of Indians prints.
Yesterday Nonah died, to-day she lives."
Thus, Wawasmoqueh, tawney maiden, spake.

Swift through the tangled wood I bent my way,
With maple, beech, and festoon'ry
Of scarlet trumpet flowers, o'ercanopied;
Trampling on forest blossoms, peeping out
From beds of moss, disputing thus with me,
The way to Weesaw's lodge, on a green bank,
Bathed by St. Joseph's limpid tide.

In groups,
On the smooth turf, in attitudes of ease,
Were scattered manly forms of dusky hue,
With gorgeous drapery, carelessly enrobed;
Where games, and sport, and laugh, and savage shout
Sent terror on the half-unpractised ear.
With timid step, I passed those gamesters by,
And in the Indian wigwam, wondering, gazed!
Before an unclasped casket, Nonah stood—
Death had unloosed his grasp, and poised his lance;
To suffer one more, eager, raptured gaze
On tinselled trinket, silver rings and beads!

Slowly I measured back my shaded way;
And while I lingered mid the wooing flowers,
That o'er my hand laid their long waving stems;
Or plucked the rich wild fruits that round me glowed;
Thought how the workings of the unlettered mind
Assimilated, in their fancies strange,
To fairer, wiser beings, far away,
Beyond the eastern borders of the lakes—
How the extremes of highly polished life,
And life untamed, were in each other merged;
Sighing for revel, pageantry and glare—
Leaving the simple charm of happiness,
For those retired and tranquil middle walks,
Where time sweeps by, with such a measured wing,
As leaves from active duties, ample space
For the luxurious leisure of the mind;

To rise in the Divinity of thought;
Regale with zest on wisdom's lettered page,
Expand in easy, graceful song—to feel
The purest bliss of making others blest.

At night, the drum beat for the wabina;*
Venison sent forth its savory odor through
The Chieftain's hall; and there, his Indian Queen,
With brow vermillioned, and with jewels crowned;
Sandled with gaily broidered mocasin—
Nonah *alive, danced at her own death-wake.*

---

*Festival and dance of the Pottowattamies.

### WINTER IN THE WEST

WHY are our enjoyments less appreciated under their immediate influences, than when viewed over the waste, where memory loves to stray, and collect the glowing beauties that Time has scattered from his wing? A tone the most exquisite, often falls on some chord that vibrates only for the past; and the rarest flower may send out an odor only to remind us of some pleasure withdrawn. The calm complacency felt on contemplating a piece of art, perfect in coloring and proportion, equals not the pain which averts the eye, when it meets there the slightest interruption to harmony.

Who can solve the spirit's mysteries? Philosophy may unfold the cool discipline of her schools, and teach us calmly to yield to the discordances of life; to find our enjoyments in the present hour. There is a higher power that permits our minds to flash and scintillate, when met by opposing elements; that alone can guide their erratic, restless wanderings, that knows our aspirations for something beyond the present period, beyond the attritions of earth, where the repose of full fruition requires not the mellowing power of retrospection, nor the tintings of hope.

This chain of reflections is closely linked in with the feelings of the hour, when a wintry scene in the West, forcibly contrasts itself with that southern clime, vivid on the memory as its evergreens, where genial suns and warm friendships have shed their hues on the path of life.

The prairies which have been described when the flowers blow and the birds sing, now spread out a winter piece, if not so lovely, yet sublimely beautiful. These interminable plains, covered over with snow, seem like a vast frozen ocean, whose surface lays unmoved by the bleak winds that sweep over it. Yesterday unfolded one of those unrivalled pictures, which nature, in her fitful moods, sometimes hangs out to view. A slight, drizzling rain had, in falling, congealed, and clung to the branches of trees in a surrounding grove; presenting in the sun's rays, a foliage sparkling with every hue of the rainbow. These, with their accumulated weight, as the day advanced, yielded in their brittleness; and under this stealthy operation through the forest, the trees seemed responding to each other, as their profuse and wealthy burthens fell showering to the ground. As night approached, heavy peals of thunder mingled with the falling of icicles, while vivid flashes of lightning, at times, lit up the glittering boughs. The rain poured down in torrents and, in one night, all this

ephemeral splendor was drenched away.
With the morning sun, no traces are left of
the beautiful pencilling of frost.   Transient
as the world's glory that beams and dazzles,
to be swept away with a crash, in the dark
and stormy night of adversity.

*"Sic transit gloria mundi."*

Come, come out all loved ones, and view with me,
　　How resplendent the trees appear!
Come quickly, you never again may see
　　Such beauty as sparkles here.

The rain that descended in torrents, last night,
　　On the dry, leafless boughs, hangs congealed;
And a frostwork is glittering, more dazzlingly bright,
　　Than winter has ever revealed.

Every shrub, with its burthen of pure, crystal gems
　　In their newness, is covered o'er;
As if shaken from angel's diadems—
　　All along the frozen white shore.

How these jewels of purest water, shine,
　　Reflecting each changeful hue
Of the glorious sky, where a hand divine
　　Such enchantment hangs out to the view.

In their riches, how lowly the branches appear,
　　With fretted white garlands all crowned;
A joy seems lit up, in the glistening tear,
　　That covers their stems to the ground.

The chastened breezes seem filled with delight,
　　As through the rich foliage they play.
The sun goes down with a golden light,
　　At the close of this wintry day.

From the heart that is chill'd with the rude blasts of woe
　　Hope beams in the heaven-lit eye—
An icicle cold, may sparkle and glow,
　　When kindled with rays from on high.

LETTER TO MRS.  * * *  BUFFALO, NEW-YORK.

GALENA, Illinois, 1836.

I AVAIL myself of a leisure hour, to communicate my impressions of the country after leaving Chicago, which has been described by those better enabled to do so than myself, shut in as I was by unpleasant weather, during the few days I remained there. It is impossible not to perceive that its destiny is lofty, and its commercial advantages incalculable, though it does not seem probable they can justify the very high prices that property commands, at the present time.

The adjoining country is repulsive to agricultural prosperity. Moving westwardly, over the marshy prairies, one is naturally led to inquire, is there no way of redeeming them from their watery empire? It is possible, that by some process of draining, they may, in time, be made subservient to the interests of that new and flourishing emporium For miles, there is no appearance of a road regularly laid off; each one taking the course his judgment or experience suggests.    Passing onward, the prairies become more beautiful; no longer marshy, but gently undulating, and appear to the eye interminable. They have a striking resemblance to water, and not the less so, when one descries far off, a man on horseback, slowly moving over them, in that regular, measured pace, observable in fording a river; the outline of both, distinctly defined on the horizon, at a very considerable distance.  Groves of flourishing young growth appear at intervals, like islands in the ocean—oceans of blossoming fragrance, when the wind waves over the long luxuriant grass; and as if to keep up the illusion, that expansion of feeling is produced as when at sea; the little ills of life are lost

5*

sight of, and the mind, with the eye, takes in no views but such as are pleasurable. The lassitude of the invalid is chased away, and care and ennui vanish before the enchanting spell.

Approaching Rock river, the surface of the country becomes more uneven, and more magnificently attractive. Does any one sigh for a romantic seclusion, embowered under lofty trees, let him come to Illinois, and erect a snug cottage or pillared palace, where his grounds are more beautifully ornamented than the most fastidious and refined taste could dictate.

On either side of Dixon's ferry, on Rock river, were seen covered wagons of the enterprising emigrant, drawn by oxen, with women, sturdy urchins, cattle and sheep, finding their way to this new world. It is impossible to contemplate such a picture with indifference. A cordial welcome should, indeed, on every hand, greet these wary travellers. How little do they, in the simplicity of their views, dream of the destiny that perhaps awaits many of them. The most buoyant and playful imagination must be outstripped by the prosperity which will, at some future day, smile on this favored portion of the earth; when the hand of industry shall have elicited the wealth that is slumbering in the fertile soil, and science shall have reared her temples in these western groves.

Within thirty miles of Galena, the aspect of the country changes; green hills, covered with light timber, are frequently seen; and rocks, piled one upon the other, give indications that the traveller is approaching that far-famed mineral region; and in the vicinity of those exhaustless sources of wealth to the industrious adventurer.

Galena may be said to be rudely romantic. Its approach is made by descending a long winding hill, on the opposite side of the river, which commands a fine panoramic view of this *unique* little village.   It is composed of two streets, on the lower side of a crescent-shaped hill, covered to the top with wild shrubbery and rocks.   Its buildings are small and irregular; when these give place to more tasteful architecture, it will be pretty, and not less so for its eccentricity of appearance.   It is situated on *Feve* or Bean, usually called Fever river, one hundred yards wide, having sufficient water for the largest steamers navigating the upper Mississippi; whose back water extends to the village, a distance of seven miles.   On the bank of the river, opposite Galena, a volume of smoke is at all times seen curling up from a smelting establishment.   Bars of lead are piled up all along the street next to the river, ready to be transported by steamers, that ply regularly between this place and St. Louis.

To the left, arise the undulating hills of North Galena, adjoining the town, and laid off into lots to suit purchasers. They form very desirable locations for private residences, commanding an extensive view of the country around.

Galena has Episcopal, Presbyterian, Methodist and Catholic denominations of religion; two presses, and a branch of the Bank of Illinois. It has a highly respectable and intelligent population, and from its advantages present and prospective, may challenge a comparison with any of the vigorous young towns of the West.

TO MRS. * * * , BUFFALO, N. Y.

GALENA, 1836.

UNEXPECTED delay in my journey south-
ward, has afforded me an opportunity of
making some excursions over this country;
and not the least interesting, is a *pilgrimage*
I have lately made to the Falls of St. Anthony. As if the first step were to be pre-
cursive of the novel and pleasing, 11 o'clock
at night found me with my friends, on board
the fine steamer St. Peters, winding our way
over the quiet waters of Fever river, whose
elevated banks seem to have parted for the
purpose of allowing the Mississippi to steal
up this wild ravine, and bear away the productions of these mineral regions. To be
thus suddenly borne along, past shrub and
tree, and grassy cape, mirrored on the wave
by the beams of a full moon, was calculated

to create a dreamy, solemnized admiration of a scene so startling and impressive.

On the following morning we were pursuing our way up the Mississippi; the bold, majestic outline of its mountain-barriers, emphatically pointing out the contrast with the low, monotonous shores of this river, below its confluence with the Ohio. Its alluvial points and receding curves are not seen here, nor are its waters turbid, having the hue and clearness of amber.

Cassville, a small new village in Wisconsin Territory, on the east side, about forty miles from the mouth of Fever river, is handsomely situated, on an elevated bank, about twenty feet in height; the lofty hills in the rear, forbidding any extent of size, except along the river. The mineral in its vicinity must give impulse to its prosperity.

About eight miles further, on the west side, a beautiful table land of prairie stretches along, four miles in extent, about twenty feet high, affording free navigation to a town lately laid off here, called Prairie la Porte, the unfledged nursling of adventurous speculation. Turkey river forms a part of its southern boundary; and at its northern extremity, a spring flows off with sufficient water to turn a mill; the adjacent land is fertile, and unless checked by some unforeseen cause, this spot cannot fail to attract the attention of the enterprising emigrant.

Prairie du Chien, about thirty miles above, is situated on a smooth level surface, its shores gradually descending to the water. Fort Crawford is built of stone, and has, at present, five companies of fifty men. The village, a little further on, consists of a few indifferent houses, and is a depot for stores sent on to the garrison. The bold undulations in the rear of Prairie du Chien, covered with vegetation, without shade, are so peculiarly thrown together, as to produce an imposing effect. An active imagination might trace in their outlines, a resemblance to spacious tents, so disposed as to suggest the idea of a grand military encampment, which, in the vicinity of the Fort, affords a pleasing coincidence. On the shore, in front of the village, was assembled a number of vagrant Winnebago Indians, in the wretchedness that attends them when hovering on the verge of civilization—squalid, half naked, their faces disfigured, and hideous with streaks of black and red paint—wrecks of that native grandeur which characterizes them before an intercourse with the white man, has made them feel wants without the means of gratifying them. Their fine saddles of venison were exchanged for whiskey, which they placed in their canoes, and paddled them off to their wigwams, there to enjoy the oblivious draught.

6

After leaving Prairie Du Chien, the traveller awakes to a new interest, when he
finds he is beyond the boundary of civilized
man; that the wilderness through which he is
passing, is only tenanted by the wild natives,
or still wilder deer, panther and buffalo.

I have never contemplated nature with
features so bold and majestic, softened
down with expressions of such enchanting
sweetness.   Lofty hills on either side of the
river; some conical, some less pointed,
others beautifully rounded off, seem like
mountain-waves or swells which heave the
bosom of the ocean in a storm, becoming
suddenly fixed and motionless.   On the
summit of many of these hills, immense
rocks are imbedded; presenting, at a distance, the appearance of forts, castles, tow-
ers, broken columns; with every thing that
fancy can conceive of ruins, in lonely grandeur; with vines clustering over them, and

often, in their luxuriance, almost screening them from the view. Beneath some of the projecting cliffs are seen, what might seem to be the remains of ancient walls, lying along, with little interruption for miles. Sometimes, verdant undulations appear, without tree or shrub, succeeded by others covered with a dense, rich foliage, with occasional light openings refreshing to the eye.

About forty miles above Prairie du Chien, we went on shore, to view the ground where the battle of "Bad Axe" was fought, in 1832, decisive of the war with the Sauk and Fox Indians. In the dark forest, almost overgrown with underwood, the grave, which encloses the bodies of five soldiers who fell there, was pointed out by an officer who distinguished himself in the engagement. Left an offering of flowers. Poor fellows! No stone marks the spot where ye repose, and soon no vestige will appear to claim the sigh of the passing traveller.

It is a singular feature of the country, that on the summit of the mountains, are uninterrupted prairies of a descent so gradual as to be imperceptible; but sufficient to bear off the water courses in either direction. They are said to possess all the characteristics of those level wastes, diversified with woodland, numerous lakes, and covered with an endless variety of the flowery creation.

Lake Pepin, about one hundred miles below St. Peters, is a sudden expansion of the river, twenty two miles in length, and from two to four in width. The high projecting bluffs derive increased beauty and sublimity from the broad bosom of water they enclose; indented with numerous capes, stretching along in verdant luxuriance. A breeze just sufficient to ruffle the waves, tinted with the setting sun, contributed to create a pleasing excitement in passing over it.  There are many legends connected with these wild glens, that chime in with the air of romance surrounding them.  One of these lofty precipices is styled the "Maiden's Rock;" from which, tradition says, a Sioux girl, named We-no-na, precipitated herself, to elude the destiny prepared for her by her parents, of being united to a warrior; having already given her heart to a young hunter.

From the great depth of Lake Pepin, it may not be unreasonable to conclude that it has some rocky bed, from which issue springs, or some vast spring, ever gushing up, contributing to the strangeness of these wonder-stirring regions.  Fine specimens of cornelian and agate are found on the beach of the Lake.

Mississippi! flowing on in thy majestic course, a distance of three thousand miles, through the fairest valley in the world; receiving innumerable tributary streams; bearing over thy waves the productions of many soils, on to the ocean, for remote eastern climes—how many water courses have been familiarly carried home to the minds of men, by description; while thou, for ages, hast rolled on in thy mighty grandeur, receiving little more than a passing tribute of admiration. Is it that thy wonders bid defiance to description? That song, in its loftiest flight, dare not approach thee? The most happily graphic pen must pause, and the pencil drop from the hand, when the eye is raised to thy lofty magnificence, or reposes on the magic revellings of nature, over the wave-lashed freshness of thy shores, and thy islands of beauty. A sketch, though imperfect, might at least allure the curious and idle tourist to vary his oft-travelled eastern route, and visit these regions, possessing in so high a degree the charm of novelty; more

exhilarating than the sparkling fountains of
Saratoga; with airs balmy and salubrious,
and scenery which might cause pleasurable
excitement, even for those who have lingered round Niagara's own flood. The contemplation of thy pictorial beauties creates
a visionary existence from which one fears
to awake too soon; and the mind feels an
avaricious desire to prolong sensations, that
so rarely enrich the monotonous waste.

Drawing nearer to the head of navigation, Indian villages appear, so located as
to evince their innate sense of the tasteful
and desirable. The wigwams, at these
places, are deserted at this season of the
year; their pursuits and propensities leading them to frequent change of residence.

One of these beautiful openings bears the
name of Prairie la Croix, where the Sioux
assemble for recreation in some of their
favorite games. On another, is seen a small

rock of bright red, where the Indians leave offerings of arrows and tobacco. Their singular sepulture is often witnessed in passing along. The body is enclosed in a wooden box, covered with a white blanket, and placed on a scaffold about ten feet from the ground. Somewhere in the vicinity of this place, a ledge of grey rock stretches along the edge of the water, on which "Catlin" is painted in red letters.

The approach to Fort Snelling is highly imposing. It stands on a high promontory, sloping down to the water; having a foundation of rock with a substratum of pure, white sand stone. The river St. Peters passes by on one side, the Mississippi on the other. A garrison of United States troops is stationed here, consisting of five companies, commanded by Col. Davenport, who has a fine airy residence within the Fort; the tower in front of which commands

a view, embracing an island covered with
the richest luxuriance, the confluence of the
two rivers, and the high grounds beyond,
inexpressibly beautiful.

Here, at the head of navigation, a spot
replete with interest; under the roar of Fort
Snelling's artillery, we passed the anniver-
sary of American Independence—the native lords of the soil bringing baskets of
strawberries to exchange for bread, or lying along the shore; their bosoms feeling no
patriotic glow; careless of the present and
happily unconscious of the future.

A morning ride of eight miles over a high
prairie country, brought in view the Falls of
St. Anthony.  Here the Mississippi presents
a wide, smooth sheet of water, moving
calmly on, as if quietly collecting its forces,
ere it arrives at the rocky projection, extending entirely across; uneven, and broken
off in various shapes, apparently suited to

the rocks, lying piled beneath, in every possible form; some of immense magnitude.
Over these, the water makes a sudden
bound, throwing up clouds of snow-white
spray. Intervening slips, covered with light
vegetation, separate the flood into three di-
visions; that on the eastern side has the
greatest descent, about twenty-two feet, and
being less impeded by rocks, forms a full
unbroken tide. A short distance below the
Falls, an island is formed of huge masses
of rocks; from their shape, creating the impression that they have been torn from the
precipice above, and carried by the stream
to their present bed; these, sheltered with
trees and vines, and terminating in a point
of land, present a picturesque view.

Thoughts that arise while ascending the
upper Mississippi, are more forcibly impressed by the contemplation of appearances
around this spot. The elevation of the

land, over a level surface, seems to indicate that its waters were once spread over the country in small lakes or ponds, constituting its source; until by some convulsion of nature, an outlet was formed by the rending asunder of the earth; thus opening a mighty ravine for their egress, receiving accumulation from other streams, and continuing to flow on through a lengthened valley, till they found their way to the ocean.

All descriptions of the Falls of St. Anthony with the wild and picturesque scenery surrounding it, must be tame and spiritless compared with the reality. The mind is filled with a humble and awe-struck admiration; and intuitively turns to that Power that "hath measured the waters in the hollow of his hend, and weighed the hills in a balance."

Rock Castle, Near Nashville, Ten.

I write from an eminence, commanding a panoramic view of the beautiful "city
of rocks;" its tall spires glittering in the
sun; its evergreen environs, sprinkled over
with rural cottages; in simple contrast with
stately edifices, surrounded with tastefully
improved grounds. The view includes that
classic spot, long since denominated "College Hill," whence an intellect of the most
towering order, is diffusing its elevating influence over the rising community; commanding a fine prospect, in which the Cum-
berland river is seen on its way past the rude
cliffs on which the city stands. On the left,
low cultivated vales lie quietly along; the
whole terminating in a distant mountain
boundary.

The view before me derives heightened interest from being associated with my first impressions of western enterprise and high-toned character; awakening reminiscences of the lights and shadows of fortune, and the enchantments of *home.* There, with friends of happy memory, I have whiled away the time too long, and I hasten to send you the continuation of my tour on the Upper Mississippi. While I am aware that the vivid impressions made by actual observation, cannot be imparted, I hope the information they may convey will not be unacceptable.

Before taking leave of the beautiful frontier regions, I visited that section of them, called the mining district, in Wisconsin Territory. For twenty miles from Galena, nothing is presented to diversify the general aspect of the country, except three isolated hills, called "Platte Mounds," rising about half a mile distant from each other; the two largest, about a mile in circumference, regularly rounded off, and covered with scattered shrubbery and rocks. The one in the centre is of a conical form, entirely bare, except light vegetation and projecting rocks on one side. These sudden elevations, on a wide extended waste, are, in their outlines, distinctly visible for several miles in every direction, and very happily relieve the monotony that every where surrounds them. Their size forbids the idea that they can be any other than monuments of the eccentricity that nature here seems to delight in.

Near these, stands the new town of Belmont, containing a few houses, erected by the principal proprietor, so commodious and pleasantly situated, as to have allured the first convention of a legislative council in the territory, of which the brave Dodge, of Indian war memory, is the Governor.

From this onward, lead mines, or in the

*technical* language of the miners, *diggings*, frequently meet the view. The mineral is excavated and thrown out, adhering to earth or yellow ochre, from which it is separated at the smelting houses, where, by fusion, it is formed into bars for exportation. One frequently meets loads of it, in its rude state, drawn by eight oxen. It is asserted that a thousand men, in a thousand years, would fail to exhaust these mines—mines of gold and silver, literally they are not; but they are flowing out in streams, that may inundate these regions with all the blessings wealth can bestow.

Mineral Point, thirty-five miles from Galena, is a small town, consisting of very indifferent houses; with its rude, unobtrusive appearance on the lower side of a hill, nothing pleasing is connected, except what arises from the prospective view of its prosperity.

Lofty hills in the rear of Dubuque, in Iowa, not far distant, on the western shore of Mississippi river, also teem with mineral; their towering height seeming to boast that a city might be excavated from them, springing from its mountain cover, more fresh and surprising, though perhaps less pleasing to the virtuoso, than the splendid antiquities men are now disinterring in the far east.

This flourishing village has sprung into existence since the war of 1832, with the Sauk and Fox Indians, who then relinquished their claim to the soil. It has a landing for steam-boats, a press and Presbyterian church. It derives its name from a Frenchman, who about half a century ago, found his way into the confidence of the Indians, and blended his fortunes, as his bones are now mingled with theirs. On the summit of a stupendous mountain cliff, overhanging the Mississippi, in bold relief with a quiet

vale, presenting the ruins of an Indian village, stands the "tomb of Dubuque." It is
surmounted with a wooden cross, bearing
a simple inscription; as if to perpetuate the
fellowship, near him repose the remains of
a Warrior Chief, beneath a covering of
slabs; both enshrouded under the verdant
leaf, through which the winds murmur a
gentle dirge to these children of nature.

It was not without regret that I bade farewell to Galena, where I had sojourned during the summer. A lively recollection remains of the view from an upper gallery, of
the stage daily winding its way down the
hill; with the almost hourly arrival of steam-
boats, bringing visitants to the land of promise; the hotels affording the anomaly of
comforts with privations; privileges with
inconveniences; curious machines, receiving
and pouring out a continual rotation of busy
life: each day furnishing a new set of faces,

with land speculation impressed upon them in legible characters.

The first striking feature that arrests the attention on entering the Mississippi, is Rock Island, covered with dense luxuriance. Fort Armstrong stands at its southern extremity, having a foundation of solid rock; a natural fortress, sternly imposing, seeming to bid defiance even to the attacks of time. A low arch in the rock, appears as if leading to some subterraneous cave. The river sweeps boldly along at its base.

Within sight of the Fort, stands Rock Island city, on an elevated prairie; the northern point washed by Rock river, where it empties into Mississippi. With this spot, interesting and melancholy associations are connected. Wandering over it, an involuntary sigh arises, when we reflect that this was the loved home of Black Hawk and his forefathers; that for more than a century, here stood the village where they roamed, free as their own native air. Here, have they fondly lingered around their family fires, their altars, and the graves of their fathers; whence they could not be severed without the sacrifice of many lives, and more than a million of our nation's money. A laudable feeling has suggested the design of erecting a monument in the centre of the town, to the memory of the brave warriors, whose bones are to be collected and there entombed.

From Wabisipinica, or White Swan, nine miles above the Rapids, to Mascoutine Island, a distance of forty miles, the western shore presents scenery of unrivalled loveliness. Though nature, for five hundred miles above, has been prodigal of her wonders, and has strung along, her alpine hills, her cliffs, and her frowning battlements, here, she has not been more sparing of her milder beauties. An affluence of arcadian scenery enriches the shores with all the garniture of fresh and solitary sweetness; more attractive than when the period arrives that will proudly say, art has been here. Eminences, sloping gently down to the margin of the water, are, in some places, covered with groves of dense foliage; on others, trees are standing out in all the charm of light and shade, while intervening vales lie along, most seducing to the settler's view.

Near Rock Island, at the foot of one of these slopes, quietly reposes the infant town of Davenport; a smile of complacency, almost prophetic, seems to settle around this commerce-inviting depot.

Rockingham, a few miles below, is also a desirable location, possessing advantages which will ensure it, at least, a share of the prosperity that awaits these embryo towns. There are countless numbers of these new aspirants, inviting the enterprising emigrant to halt with his steam-propelled house, already prepared and fitted to be put together in a few days after he arrives at his new home. A particular description of these places could not create that lively interest and admiration that is felt, while gliding past them, on that element that is to make them, ere long, "arrogant young cities of the west."

The Lower Rapids commence one hundred and fifty miles below Rock Island. The time taken up in lightening the boat by transferring lead, and about sixty passengers, to a small keel boat, afforded an opportunity of walking along the shore, and picking up some fine specimens of crystallized quartz. Much force is required to break them open, and on yielding their lustre to the light, they seem like those virtues that sparkle brightest under the strong arm of oppression.

The Rapids present no unusual appearance, except a slight rippling of the water; but it is hardly possible to divest one's self of anxiety, when the vessel is heard striking against the rocks, which, at a low stage of water, the most skilful navigator cannot wholly avoid. The "Upper Rapids" are eighteen miles in extent, the "Lower Rapids" twelve. At the termination of them, is a small village, called Keokuk, belonging to a band of Sauk Indians, who have a reservation extending a considerable distance along the west side of the river.

Mascoutine Island lays, for about twenty miles, like a luxuriant meadow; its tall flowers forming an entire purple surface. Many remains of Indian encampments are seen near the shore. The tents are formed of arched saplings, most of them dismantled of their covering, save here and there a portion of their bark remnants floating in the air. One cannot but contemplate these soli-

tary ruins, emblems of their blasted hopes,
but with as deep interest as those of more refined nations—and almost sees them pursuing
the deer over this fragrant island.

I wish I could place before you a view
I witnessed at sunrise, near this place, with
all its claims to admiration. Near the termination of a range of hills, a cluster of trees,
with massy foliage, stood on the point of a
prairie Island; every leaf was baptized with
dew; the sun was tinging the topmost branches, while those below, lay in deep shade;
flowery arcades sent forth a balmy incense.
Through innumerable small islands, the
movement of the vessel seemed ever opening some new view of the distant water. It
was a perfect picture; and I thought there
could be no holier altar for praise and divine adoration!

A little further on, is Fort Des Moines,
composed of slight buildings, thrown up for

defence during the war on the frontiers with
the Sauk Indians. Not far below this, the
Des Moines river empties into the Mississippi. A few miles up this stream, is the present residence of Black Hawk and a few of
his followers.

Grafton, about fifty miles above St. Louis,
is very eligibly situated at the junction of
Illinois and Mississippi rivers.

The next object of attention is a settlement of a few French villagers; with this
place, is connected a traditionary account,
stating that many years ago, the Sauks
warred with the Sioux, and pursued them to
this spot, where they had encamped. To
elude their pursuers, they carried their canoes, with their little property, across a strip
of land, two miles in width, between the
Mississippi and Missouri rivers, and followed up the latter in safety. Thus originates
the name of the village, *Portage Des Sioux*.

Alton, a flourishing town in Illinois, is about twenty miles above St. Louis. Not far from this, the Missouri river falls into the Mississippi, retaining the name, but bearing along with it, the irregular features and gloomy character of the former.

St. Louis lies beautifully along the river, about two miles, extending back three quarters of a mile. The lapse of near a century, has left but few traces of its original appearance. The northern part of the city has many elegant buildings, and some tastefully improved situations. It is shaded with tall forest trees; some of them, perhaps, planted by the simple wanderers, early attracted to this spot. Natural mounds in the vicinity, afford a fine prospect of the river, and country mansions embowered under deep groves.

St. Louis has twelve thousand inhabitants; and forty steamers frequently lying along in front of fine large stone warehouses, confirm the assertion, that it has, within a few years, received a new impulse. It possesses immense resources, rapidly developing in Missouri, Illinois, Iowa and Wisconsin, pouring down mineral and other productions, all seeking a vent through the bold watercourses that beautifully vein their several states and territories, and pressing onward to the Mississippi.

It is easy to perceive, that the present and increasing prosperity of this, and other towns in the west, is indebted to the industry of the enterprising emigrant. A welcome hand should be extended to them, and it is well that a jealous care watches over them, to protect them from the monied speculator, indulging at ease, in reveries of unbounded wealth, flowing from whole sections of land, lying waste and uncultivated.

In descending the river from St. Louis,

the shores diminish in beauty; and little more
than a continued wilderness meets the eye.

The confluence of the Ohio with the Mississippi, forms a broad expanse of water; for
a considerable distance, these two majestic
bodies roll along, side by side, retaining their
distinct hue; and seem proudly reluctant to
the union; until, at length, the clear, trans-
lucent stream is lost in Mississippi's dark
and turbid wave. As the vessel turned its
course into the Ohio, it was not without emotion, that I cast a parting look on the "Father
of rivers."

ILLINOIS, 1839.

LEAVING Lake Michigan, at Chicago, I have again been travelling over prairies so vast as almost to seem like a continuation of ocean beauties. At length, I am awakened to the reality that I am reposing on the borders of the far-famed Rock river, and at leisure to send you a few brief sketches of my tour on the Northern Lakes.

I intuitively turn to the morning when the Buffalo moved majestically out of the harbor to which it owes its name; when every eye was turned to the receding beauties of the queenly city; when its busy commerce, its inviting shores and rural environs were soon lost in Lake Erie's wide expanse.

From Detroit, an unclouded sky smiled on our course through Lake St. Clair, and

the transparent blue waters of the bolder
Huron. The contemplation of these vast
inland seas, creates an expansion of thought
and feeling. Their monotony is happily
relieved by islands of various sizes; among
which is Presque Isle; its pebbly shores
shaded with evergreen. The Manitou Isles
are hallowed in the minds of the children of
the forest; being, as they believe, the favorite haunts of the Great Spirit. Some islands
have Indian encampments spread over them,
where they resort for their favorite amusements of hunting and fishing.

The visit to Makina being reserved for our
return, we pursued our course, winding past
high promontories; the shores covered with
dense forests, chiefly evergreen; till at length
the eye is greeted with a distant view of the
anxiously looked for Sault de St. Marie. On
a near approach, merely rapids are seen, leap-
ing sportively over the rocks, throwing up

8*

snow-white foam; seeming joyously to welcome the pilgrims reposing at their feet.

The little settlement on the left, consists
of small white-washed houses, scattered
along on a gentle green elevation. Many of
these are inhabited by people commingling
a French and Indian origin, and speaking
the former language. Amphibious, they
may almost be called, so great is their fondness of the water. Under the appellation of
*voyageurs*, they row the birch canoes for
those who wish to enter the bay above the
falls, or penetrate into the Lake, with their
oars keeping time with their songs. A canal passes by their doors, as a means of
communication with Lake Superior.

The Fort is enclosed by a rough palisade;
the buildings are white, every thing wearing
a neat and pleasing air, with a smooth green
area in the centre.

Further back, is a Mission station, where

I was much interested in the exercises of the young natives, in reading, grammar and arithmetic. The Missionary remarked that the little community at Sault de St. Marie were united and very happy. Shut in by ice and snow for six months of the year, they receive but two mails from the civilized world. These are conveyed by an Indian on foot, adventurously breasting the weather, exposed to storms, fatigue and privations, for the gratification of those isolated people; listless of the interest contained in the little budget at his back.

Mr. J., father-in-law of the distinguished S., has a pleasant situation on the confines of the village. His wife, in the costume of her nation, speaking only their language, large and stately, visited the steam-boat with her daughters, refined and intelligent women, dressed with much taste and fashion. Crowds of Chippewas, or Ogibwas, came on board to welcome the arrival of the pale faces.

The soil is cold, and unfavorable to cultivation, not affording sufficient duration of the sun's warmth to mature the growth of corn. The fir, the cedar and the pine, serve as a defence from the winds of winter, and are most vivid when contrasted with the broad mantle of snow, which for half the year is spread over these northern regions. On its crusted surface the inhabitants walk, with their large, flat snow shoes, formed of net-work; or ride in sledges, drawn by dogs, gaily caparisoned with ribbons, beads and little bells.

An intense interest pervades the mind here, in the vicinity of Lake Superior, spread out in lonely grandeur, its silence unbroken, save by the wild tenants of the forest shore, or the paddling of the Indian canoe, as it skims over the crystal wave; so transparent, that its white pebbles may be seen at the depth of forty feet. At lengthened intervals, the fur-laden vessel moves over it, and the solitary tourist lingers around the pictured rocks that overhang its shores. In its cold, northern position, thus for ages has it been, and thus perhaps for ages will it be, forever flowing on to the ocean.

Retracing our course, a few hours brought us in sight of the island of Makina, rising like a fairy mound out of the waves. It is nine miles in circumference. The promi-nent object in approaching it, is the famed Arch Rock, standing out in bold relief, from the back ground of a dark forest, crested with lofty trees. Fort Makina, with its white buildings, stands beautifully on the side of the mountain. Still higher, perhaps five hundred feet from the base of the hill, are the remains of the old Fort, commanding a fine view of the little village lying along the shore;

the waters stretching away with their green islands, some in the distance, melting in the blue wave.

The houses are indifferent, many of them in a state of dissolution; more than a century having elapsed since their erection by those early settlers, who have left eloquent testimonials of their taste in all their wanderings.

To Arch Rock, all repair to gaze and admire; its immense masses of rocks of various shapes, towering up and sheltered beneath dark foliage. Here, the Algonquin Chiefs, on their arrival, enquired for the sacred Rock, being told by tradition, that the setting sun passed under its arch.

Could the spirit of De la Martine hover around this island, with its bewildering mazes of tangled underwood, its sequestered glens overhung with maple, birch and cedar; how many might be induced to repair here, to witness what no other pencil, perhaps, could paint so well—other fancies may brighten at its poetry of rock and shade, and sky-reflected wave, and wish for the power of graphic pen to express what they can only feel; but it will serve for a bright picture to set in opposition to some of the darker shades on memory's tablets.

On turning away, the Buffalo was soon careering over the wild and restless Lake Michigan, on towards Green Bay.   On approaching this port, the peculiarly soft, lively verdure of the grassy islands and slips of land stretching out into the water, clearly conveys the appropriateness of its name. The houses of the village are simple in structure; the ground on which they stand forming a gentle curve; every thing around wears an inviting air of repose.   The elevated grounds in the rear will, in time, serve as desirable locations for private residences.

Milwaukee was the last object of interest that presented itself. This lively and vigorous little village furnishes an instance among the many, of the successful results which attend the efforts of the emigrant, in forming new homes in the west; where, whether he be farmer, mechanic, teacher, physician, statesman or ecclesiastic, he will find a wide sphere for future usefulness. Milwaukee has, within four years, risen up from an entire wilderness, which continues with little variation, along the western side of the Lake, on to Chicago.

## THE BASKET MAKER.

### TO * * * * .

#### SARATOGA.

I am now looking out on the flowing fes-
toonery of vines that cover the pillars of
Congress Hall. The rooms have lately
been thrown open for the reception of visitors, of whom few have yet assembled; and
those, principally such as would prefer the
cool, airy neatness and quiet that now pre-
vail, to the bustle and excitement that per-
vade a congregated mass of human passions.
The fresh green of the trees, and the air of
tranquillity that breathes around, render the
place peculiarly congenial with the langour
of the invalid. The company may be said
to be chiefly composed of exclusives, loung-
ing about in that easy dishabille manner,
which is certainly more convenient than the

customary exactions of fashion and ceremony.

My friends have just directed my attention
to an old man who stepped on the piazza
below, with some baskets for sale.   A group
of politicians were sitting there.   One of
them purchased a basket for his little child,
at fifty per cent. less than its original price,
saying it was enough for the present hard
times.

Thinking by way of variety, to have some
little amusement with the old man, they
questioned him respecting his politics; one
of them asking him how he voted.   He
scrutinized them for a few moments, from
under his large straw hat, and at length gave
them some shrewd, though evasive answer.
They then asked him if he knew that Gen.
Jackson was the cause of his manufacture
selling for less than its value; to which he
replied:

"Well, I'm thinking that gentlemen travelling to these springs, can afford to pay me for my wares."

One of them observed, "I'll venture to say you have more money than I have."

"As to that I know not; but I guess I'm worth as much as two thirds that come here, if their debts were paid. As you wish to know something about my politics, I have no objection to telling you; for I'm no way ashamed of 'em."

Here, the old man threw himself into an attitude for declamation, quite unexpected to his audience, and with "action suited to the word" thus addressed them:

"Gentlemen, I lived in Gen. Washington's time, and he was the greatest man that ever lived in these United States. Well, he had a kind of currency put in circulation, called continental money. You know all about it as well as I can tell you. The people complained of hard times; but in the end, all turned out well. A great deal of good often grows out of some evil." Raising his arm, and gesticulating emphatically, he exclaimed, "men, now-a-days, wear as much fine broadcloth and trimmings, at one time; and women as much silk and laces as would buy a farm in Michigan or Illinois. Have fine carriages and rich tables, that nothing but old England could stand. Why, they tell me, that one lord or duke, there, could buy up half the nobility of New York. Their farmers are coming over here to work our waste lands, while the people here are living by head work; but it wont do. If we got more of the foreigner's money for our produce, and less of their gewgaws and wines, we should be more what Republicans ought to be; but I hope things will come right; and after a while that every man will be able to sit under his own vine and fig tree, and none to make him afraid. Gentlemen, I wish you all well." Here he gathered up his baskets and withdrew. His remarks were not without their point; and the joke turned on the old man's political opponents.

This conversation heard from an open window, carried along with it the agreeable conviction, that information, through the happy medium of the press, is diffused through every part of our republic; penetrating even to the humble cottage of the mountain basket maker.

9*

### NEENAH OR FOX RIVER.

"How beautiful!" I exclaimed, as the setting sun was bathing the rich foliage of trees,
that threw their lengthened shadows over
the borders of Fox river. "Can all the magnificence that art has spread over eastern
cities—can the loftiest monuments, or the
ruins of the old world compare with this?"
This tribute of admiration was unconscious-
ly paid to the rural environs of the little village of Aurora; which with its small houses
and large mills, soon met the view. Though
its dawnings are feeble, the fertile country
around gives it claims to future prosperity.

Following the southern course of the river,
the attention is called to the different aspect
of the country on the opposite shores. On
the one hand, trees overloaded with vines,
form a canopy of shade over the undulating

borders; further back, dark groves of oak, with occasional openings of flower-blushing prairies, skirted with forests in the distance, seeming almost blended with the blue sky; altogether spread out a landscape of enchanting beauty.

Fording the river about fifteen miles below Aurora, a ride along the western shore, over uninterrupted savannas, so level, as to make a carriage seem almost self-propelled, afforded infinitely more enjoyment than a rail-road flight; as with perfect security, it dealt out on either hand, such a prospect as one avariciously wishes to retain rather than to be snatched away with the speed of twenty miles an hour.

This section of country very happily exemplifies the effects of the pre-emption law; extending its protection to honest, industrious settlers, who have left their native homes, with nothing but helpless families and bold,

adventurous hearts. Amply are they enti-
tled to the complacency with which they
must look over their wide fields, their well
filled garners and their large stacks of hay.

Every where, does the western world
hold out attractions for the enterprising; and
to those who have felt the chilling frowns of
fortune, seems to say, come hither, and forget artificial wants in the enjoyment of substantial blessings. Under your own vine,
learn the philosophy so cheerfully inscribed
on simple, unadorned cabins, that however
small the circle of human wishes may be
drawn, comfort and peace may dwell within.

Taking a view through the future vista of
half a century, it seems highly probable that
the whole course of Fox river will be bor-
dered with one continued village, with highly cultivated fields, orchards and vineyards,
extending back over a large extent of country. The productions of the lands will,

perhaps, in that length of time, find outlets through rail-roads, to the canal, now prematurely commenced in the vicinity of this place, connecting lake Michigan with Illinois river. The time cannot be far distant, when the deep solitudes of the trackless wastes spread far away, will be enlivened with the hum of busy enterprise, and covered over with a hardy industrious population; when science and the arts will move hand in hand over this great western empire; and incense will arise from a thousand sacred altars. When the bold water-courses that fertilize these regions, will be connected with Mississippi and the Northern lakes; the grand highways for communication with the ocean, on our southern and eastern coasts.

But though imagination may thus spring away in visions of the future, it returns chastened, and quietly folds its wings, to the contemplation of the pristine beauty that revels over these shores, which can never be more touchingly attractive than in their un-pruned, wild luxuriance along the borders of Fox river.

### VISIT TO THE ROBIN'S NEST.

In an excursion the following year over some of the eastern part of Illinois, a portion of the route lay along the borders of Fox river, diversified with golden harvests of wheat, falling under the reaper's hand; oceans of corn, waving their newly formed plumes, and herds of fine cattle grazing the fresh herbage; all furnishing a convincing evidence of the flourishing condition of these hardy industrious settlers.

So abundant are the crops, that it is estimated a very small portion will be required for the consumption of the state; the surplus productions naturally flowing off to distant markets.

The enclosures of farms are frequently formed by throwing up the sods; which, in some places, supply the deficiency of tim-

ber, and the trenches thus left, serve to drain
the superfluous moisture of the soil.    These
are soon covered with grass; and being
often sown with locust seed, make fine
hedges.

The country around Ottawa, eighty miles
south of Chicago, presents a landscape of
startling magnificence.    Verdant slopes are
covered with clumps of trees of the richest
luxuriance; others detached, so as to throw
their shade fully around them; stretching
away over vales, watered by Illinois and
Fox rivers, flowing along like rivals, at no
great distance from each other; the latter
affording glimpses of its swift, limpid water
through the overhanging foliage, leaves no
room for hesitation as to its superior claim
to admiration.

Surely here is much to tempt the idle
tourist to unloose the zone of fashion, and
come and drink at these pure fountains,

where no tumultuous passions are infused in the draught.

Near this place, I saw one of the coal mines which are so abundant in this state.

From Ottawa to Peru, a distance of sixteen miles, the country presents singular features. The road passes over a rich bottom land, nearly a quarter of a mile in width; bounded on either hand with high woodlands. Here the idea very naturally occurs, that at some former period, these low grounds must have been the bed of a large body of water, from some unknown cause, finding an outlet, through which it discharged itself, retiring along the eastern eminence. Near Peru, it takes a winding course, and sweeping past a point of land, passes along the base of a broken rude bluff, on which stands this small irregular village, containing about seven hundred inhabitants. The contemplated canal, connecting Lake Michigan with Illinois river, terminates at this place. The great quantity of rock lying here, already prepared, reminds one of the vast sums the state has expended towards an object, which in the present state of affairs, must look forward to an indefinite period for its completion. Had it gone into operation, it would have opened a mine of wealth to these enterprising Peruvians.

Between Ottawa and Peru, one of those eccentricities that often present themselves here, is invested with peculiar interest from its connexion with Indian tradition. The "Starved Rock" is composed of immense ledges, piled one upon the other, to the height of a hundred feet, presenting a semi-circular outline, partially concealed with trees and bushes, covering three fourths of an acre. Standing out in bold relief, and seen from a great distance, it forms a wild and picturesque object. Near a century ago,

it is said, two tribes of Indians were at war
with each other; the weaker party were at
length driven to entrench themselves on the
summit of this rock, inaccessible except on
one side.   Having fortified this pass, they
determined to defend themselves to the last
extremity, on their rude fortress.   One day,
attempting, as usual, to draw up water from
the river, in buckets suspended by bark, they
found the cord was severed as often as it was
let down.   The awful truth at once flashed
upon them.   The assailants had pushed
their canoes under the projecting precipice,
and with their knives, thus cut off their supply of water.   Terms of peace were, at
length, offered if they would surrender.   The
cool, sparkling element flowed on beneath
their view, mocking their agony of thirst.
The inflexibility of their natures, after long,
protracted suffering, at length gave way.
They surrendered—and the opposing tribe,

with the treachery of their nation, massacred them all, with the exception of an Indian girl, who now lives in extreme old age, at Kaskaskia, to tell the melancholy tale.

Such enduring monuments, have this un-lettered race to perpetuate their history. When the proudest pyramids of the white man are crumbled into dust; their records defaced by time, this chronicle of rock will stand out in characters of freshness, to arrest the attention of the traveller in Illinois.

The Illinois river, at a low stage, is nav-igable no higher than Peru, where the steam-boat from Peoria receiving passengers and the mail from Chicago, returns immediate-ly, a distance of seventy-five miles, to that place, pleasantly situated on the west bank of the river, about three hundred miles from St. Louis.

A ride of fourteen miles brought in view the "Robin's Nest," the high and airy residence of Bishop Chase; where every thing wears the impress of intelligence mingled with simplicity. A quiet, hallowed beauty rests over this sequestered spot; the dwelling, a temple of worship; where every sabbath, about fifty of the surrounding settlers assemble with his very interesting family; a base-viol serving as an accompaniment to the vocal music.

A slight paling encloses a lawn filled with young fruit trees; and vines partially conceal the row of log cabins which take in a fine view of the distant country. The Kikapoo river winds through a low intervening valley. On the summit of the opposite sloping grounds, under embowering shade, is seen the incipiency of an institution, which, in the hands of its benevolent founder, cannot fail of spreading a most happy influence over the State. It is styled a Theological Seminary; its primary object is to prepare

10*

young men for the ministry; not, however, to the exclusion of any who are desirous of receiving a classical education, on christian principles. It seems to stand like a cheering beacon-light in the midst of the moral wilderness that surrounds it.

This beautiful Domain of three thousand acres, was purchased by Bishop Chase, a year or two ago, at the land sales in Illinois; and seems as if expressly designed for the contemplated object. It overlooks a wide extent of country of beautiful park scenery; stretching out in soft, undulating lines. The walls of the Chapel and school house, now erecting, are in the Gothic style; and together form a cross.

Remarking that he had pointed out to me the crescent and the cross, I said they were emblematic, I feared, of the cross he would have to sustain in combatting with the infidel. "Literally so," was his reply.

Various were the reflections that crowded in, while standing by his side, within the walls of this chapel.    How many deep devotions were to ascend, and from how many young voices to the bright Heaven that shone in through the unfinished roof! Can the well-wisher of religion; can the benevolent of this nation turn aside from affording aid towards the consummation of his wishes, to establish a character for literature in the west, on a scale with the boldness of its rivers, its lakes and its prairies? And may no insinuations, such as envy but too often throws in against brilliant enterprises, entwine themselves with the honest purposes of philanthropy.    Arrows sent from the ambushed shade, are often successful when directed against the unconscious wayfarer.

On this spot selected with such a happy adaptation to its noble object; its seclusion

from worldly allurements; amid shades not
less thought-inspiring than those groves,

"Where Zeno taught and Aristotle strayed,"—

could a more painful picture be contemplated than that of the priest and the sage,
wandering around the crumbling ruins of
his hopes?

Though his disinterested zeal and untiring exertions in another quarter were not
appreciated; it is to be hoped this second
effort of self-devotion, to which even ocean
placed no barrier, will make his appeals to
an enlightened public, successful; that other
States will aid in placing this western institution on a scale commensurate with the
wishes of the venerable patriarch. It should
never be said of the State of Illinois, that
this great pioneer of literature and religion,
the first who established a regular Protes-
tant Church west of the Alleghany moun-

tains, was suffered to leave there a monument of indifference to his worth.

I have a belief, almost prophetic, that Bishop Chase will be sustained in his pious enterprise. Would that I possessed some magic key that would unlock the hearts that are closed to his appeal; or that at my bidding, the coffers of hoarded wealth would fly open, and send forth some of their contents to gild the spires of "Jubilee College."

What a feeble instrument like myself, must not hope to effect, may be brought about by that Power that rules the minds of men.

---

NOTE.—It appears from a late paper, that the Institution founded by Bishop Chase, is at this time in operation, having been materially aided by southern munificence. 1842.

## SUNDAY SCHOOLS.

"Stand in the holy places, according to the division of the families of the fathers."

On a calm sabbath morning, when every object seemed chiming in with the hallowed devotions of the hour, and all nature hymning praises to the blue Heaven above; in a low, rude edifice, a crowd was assembled, from the tender age just emerging from infancy, to the more advanced period when the expanding intellect is open to every impression. Being regularly classed, their hushed attention, and prompt, intelligent replies to questions from that book which is given us for our guide through life, most happily evinced that the budding "sentiment of religion" was there.

There, in the midst of this fold of tender lambs, stood their shepherd, with mild and placid mien, gently leading them, and dispensing that spiritual food which was to make them vigorous and healthful in their growth. This was a sabbath school, in an obscure village in Illinois.

The groups pervading the streets of cities and villages, of a Sunday morning, are often passed by with indifference, or only engage the passing attention by their beauty and innocence, or neat and cleanly attire, while they are in reality, offerings to their country, its prosperity and honor.

It is impossible to contemplate a sabbath school, judiciously conducted, without being impressed with its importance, and the beauty of its dawning usefulness. Cold must be the feelings that are not enlisted on seeing youthful girls and young men, "standing in the holy places," each with an open Bible, listening to recitations from its pages. There, in the grave and subdued garb of widowhood, with the calm, placid brow, stand the gentle, patient ones, with views of a future world, seeming to rest on the bright faces that surround them; among whom, the unconscious orphan smiles as gaily as the more favored child of fortune, blest with the fostering care of parental affection.

The attention of parents at home, is necessarily required in assisting to furnish replies to questions of deep interest, and thus coerced into reflection, they often, perhaps, feel its reaction upon themselves. The exercises over, and the important task closed of making suitable application, by pointing out the various duties in the devious walk through life; it is sweet, it is thrilling to hear the hymns arising from their tender voices, together, seeming like angel choirs. And to see them bend the pliant knee, and bow the fair head in prayer. This picture may perhaps unfold the foundation of the true popular education.

Education which has the Bible for its basis, must combine strength with beauty in its superstructure. Without this, all the theories, however splendid in their speculations, must be imperfect, and subject to the attacks of insidious enemies.

The devastation of morals, spread over *one* nation alone, through the influence of a false philosophy, the licentiousness of manners, the blind worship at the temple of pleasure, the crime and misery, are sufficient to prove that a reverence for the Bible is necessary for our prosperity and happiness not only as individuals, but as a nation.

Statistic tables plainly shew us that education, divested of accompanying religious instruction, serves not to banish crime, but merely to change its nature. Responsibilities have not that sacred weight; social duties are less binding; the same restraint up-

11

on the passions cannot exist, which the belief of future rewards and punishments, early instilled, always imposes.

The spirit of religion diffused through
science, through all the literature of the
schools, must ever have an elevating power,
causing an upward tendency towards all that
is pure and unalloyed with earthly dross.
Minds thus turned to the source of all good,
are best prepared to soar above temptation
and above the mutabilities of life.

The happy tendency of biblical instruction, is often witnessed in producing reflections that lead to an ardent desire in young
men to devote themselves to the ministry,
thus shaping their course for future usefulness

When it is generally known that these
nurseries are diffused even through the remote west, it is hoped parents will be induc-

ed more cheerfully to remove their young plants to a new soil, where the moral wilderness is already beginning to blossom as the rose.

## RIVER RAISIN.

"Ah! thou hast fled!
The brave, the gentle and the beautiful!
The child of grace and genius—"

THE river Raisin flows beautifully through the city of Monroe, forty miles from Detroit, and empties into Lake Erie, about four miles distant. It derives its name from the many grape vines growing along its borders; given to it by the French who settled there, near a century ago. Their descendants have pretty farms and modest houses along the river, with fine orchards and shrubbery, characteristic of their known taste; less ambitious of amassing wealth than of enjoying pleasant and permanent homes. The tall stately pear trees seem ancestral, and give out fruit and shade near where their forefathers now sleep.

Melancholy and hallowed associations are connected with this river. The spot was pointed out where the English, with their Indian allies crossed, when they surprised and massacred some of the noblest of our country's youth; where the brave volunteers, the chivalry of Kentucky, fell victims to savage cruelty. Soothing to their friends must be the reflection that their remains have been collected, and that a monument is to be erected to their memory, in view of the lake, where the wild flower blossoms, and the winds murmur a requiem to the early dead.

11*

### CONTRASTS.

"Is there not cause then—cause for thought,
 Fix'd eye and lingering tread;
Where, with their thousand mysteries fraught,
 E'en lowliest hearts have bled!"

THE prairies in autumn are severely contrasted with their appearance in the season, when they are only a continued bed of flowers. The first frost leaving them withered and discolored, they seem like a dreary heath, over which the bleak winds scatter the dry and rustling leaves. Being in many places set on fire, to destroy the decayed vegetation, and increase the vigor of the new; one cannot but feel apprehensive when the flames, though at a distance, are seen spreading rapidly, and threatening to circumvent him in his course. Even under such circumstances, the increased prosperity of the west, in 1842, impresses most pleasantly the traveller who, in years gone by, has seen it in the extreme infancy of its settlement. Fine farms, with substantial houses and barns, good fences, and all the indications of comfortable living, realize the most sanguine predictions.

In a late ride over the spot which was once the elysium of the Pottawattamie Indians of Michigan, admiration of the rapid strides of civilization, received a saddening check on seeing some of the deserted villages and lodges of the former lordly proprietors. Their dilapidated wigwams no longer enlivened with the drum and festive dance; the sweet, plaintive notes of the pastoral reed no longer heard; the groves which furnished an arena for athletic sports, resounding only with the woodman's axe.

Could the wandering tribes look back on their former reservation thus filled up, they would doubtless congratulate themselves that they are removed from a state so insulated, as a longer residence among the white population would produce. Since the policy of our government has rendered their removal necessary, it is pleasant to think they are happier in situations that open new and wider fields for their favorite pursuits; and to hope they will be left undisturbed in their new possessions.

The advances in agriculture, science and the arts, are every where raising monuments to the moral courage of man, leaving the home of his youth and the land of his fathers, to wield the agents of the new world, and make them subservient to his comfort and happiness.

We may penetrate these wildernesses, and perceive in many cases, how fortune, in its capriciousness, has served to people them. In humble log cabins, we may see remnants of families retired from that world

they can no longer sway. Pieces of the
massive plate which weighed down the tables of their sires, distributed in scattered
relics; a silver goblet or urn, wearing the
family coat of arms, standing out from their
mud walls; speaking of the shattered condition of the ancient splendors of their house,

"To point a moral or adorn a tale."

In many instances, are seen the descendants of those who have spent a life of luxurious ease, practising the mechanic arts; or
turning up the stubborn glebe with three
yoke of oxen.

Some in almost cloistral seclusion, filling
up intervals of leisure with favorite literary
pursuits—perhaps writing satires on the
world; while some are living on a petty sal-
ary from the government, whose independence their forefathers contributed glorious-
ly to achieve.

Sons of distinguished statesmen may be seen on these frontiers, descending the dark lead mines—retaining, however, striking marks by which they may be recognized; occasionally startling the intruder with a scintillation of the eye, speaking of their high origin; or a sudden flash elicited by some circumstance, reminding them of the dark contrast.

Such instances, however, of the vicissitudes of life, are generally attended with philosophic submission, and the true pride of independence. The preponderating class consists of industrious husbandmen, inured to toil; who, after the day's labor, lie down to enjoy sweet rest, without dreaming of the past or the future.

A voice from this teeming land has been heard across the Atlantic, and thousands of the poor and oppressed of other nations, are finding new homes in the west.

An Englishman who had immigrated to Michigan, was heard to say, he would not exchange his deer park with any of the lords in England, and that he was prouder of his lake farm, than he would be to call the King his uncle.

NEW HOMES IN 1842.

WHILE lately crossing the Northern
Lakes, my attention was called to the large
quantity of merchandize, freighting the very
fine steamers for the western country; while
at Chicago, the store houses were filled to
overflowing with the various kinds of produce designed for eastern markets.

West of Chicago, the prairies of Illinois
presented a train of wagons, loaded with
grain, and other productions of the settlers,
stimulated with the encouraging prospect
of receiving a high price for their crops of
wheat.

The country around Fox and Rock
rivers, and westward, on to Galena, which,
five years ago, disclosed little more than an
unbroken waste, is now almost entirely filled
up with smiling settlements; the land yield-

ing seventy, in some instances, a hundred bushels of corn, an acre; equally productive of other grain, and every kind of vegetation suited to a northern climate.

The weary stranger has only to enter the farm-house of one of these new settlers, ("they all entertain travellers,") to find that plenty and contentment dwell within. With the fine zest a ride over the prairies creates, he cannot but feel complacency when he sits down to their bacon and eggs, perhaps prairie hens, fresh butter, mealy, pink-eyed potatoes, and the refreshing beverage of tea or coffee, inseparable accompaniments of every meal; often deriving a charm from the easy intelligent conversation of the inmates.

It is not unusual to hear a lady from the eastern states assert, that though her domestic duties are more arduous, she would not exchange her situation for one of greater ease, that denied the prospects this new country holds out to her rising family.

"We have good schools; an excellent neighborhood within three miles round; and though a school house or barn serves, at present, for a place of worship, we hope the time is not far distant, when we shall have our church and sabbath bells, as we did in New England."

It is but too true, that the faithful itinerant preachers at the west, endure much fatigue and privation; sometimes going on foot from place to place, and stopping at a farm to labor till they have earned money enough to supply themselves with a decent garb; following the examples of those meek and humble ones, that in primitive ages, bore their cross in the wilderness.

Somonok grove on this route, with many others, having each their appropriate name, is but another term for a little village, skirted by a lengthened range of trees; with a few houses, a tavern, a blacksmith-shop and store, comprising groceries, dry goods and earthenware. It is usual for ladies to go a shopping a distance of five or ten miles, to these village groves; returning to have unqualified pleasure in displaying new dress patterns, bonnets and ribbons, to the pleased, bright faces at home.

Nature ever provident, and ever ready to minister to the tastes of man, furnishes on every hand, stores of delicious wild fruits. Strawberries, blackberries, plums, grapes, with many others, bountifully supplying the absence of those delicacies the farmer, in subduing a new soil, finds little leisure to cultivate.

The emigrant who goes to a new country with a heart braced for privation and hardship, will soon have cause to congratulate himself on his many unexpected comforts;

and can then make the important discovery, that in simplifying our wants, we appreciate our blessings—as we pause to examine with more minute attention, a solitary wild blossom, sending out its sweets on a rock, or a heath, than the assembled gaudy pomp of the flower garden. A little, silvery line of water, struggling through a glen or wild ravine, has more beautiful interest for the wanderer, than the broadest stream, receiving accumulation from numerous small rivulets, at once lost or unperceived in the mightiness of the swelling tide.

The title to the land on which Galena is situated, having been a few years ago substantiated, that city has, in consequence, made very considerable improvement in the erection of handsome and substantial buildings. The busy, bustling activity pervading the streets, affords evidence of the flourishing state of trade and commerce, resisting the pressure of a depreciated currency. The city owes its prosperity, however, chiefly to the mineral in its vicinity, and the surrounding country.

It has been asserted that millions of dollars worth of lead may be obtained from the mines in the vicinity of Dubuque. The same may, perhaps, be said of the lands adjoining Galena and Mineral Point. Aspiration for wealth, could find no better security for its realization, than in these almost inexhaustible beds of mineral, requiring only the hand of industry to transmute them into gold.

12*

## UPPER MISSISSIPPI.

"I have seen the forest-shadows lie
    Where men now reap the corn;
I have seen the kingly chase rush by,
    Through the deep glades at morn."

In a late descent on the Mississippi, while crossing the "Upper Rapids," at Sycamore Chain, the wreck of a steamboat was seen lying on its side, having sunk the day before; abandoned by its passengers, who, with their baggage, were waiting on shore, to be taken off by the first opportunity that might present. It would seem impossible not to accompany melancholy associations with this wreck; leaning on the rock that had dashed away its hopes. Yesterday, a gay and buoyant thing; enviable, careering gracefully over the waves—to-day, deserted, silent, an object of scorn, or the heartless jest; or still more mortifying pity.

The traveller, delayed on his journey, day after day, oppressed with ennui, and "hope deferred," in consequence of these obstructions, is naturally led to inquire, why is this so? It would appear that the inhabitants of a country possessing all the elements of wealth; exporting annually, millions worth of its productions, would perceive the economy of removing these obstacles to the free and unimpeded navigation of the very channel for the healthful circulation of its trade and commerce. The money so expended, were it onerous on individuals, would soon find its way back from the reduced prices of freight, while it would relieve the faithful guardians of their property from their great solicitude for its safe conveyance, as well as the risk of their vessels. To this may be added, the weighty consideration, that the greater facilities by the way of the northern lakes, are already beginning to divert trade as well as travelling in that direction.

Near the Rapids, a family of German emigrants had just landed at the small town of Warsaw, with their little effects; consisting of chests, beds, bedsteads, tables, &c., transported across the Atlantic. These shores are, indeed, covered with a checkered population. Swiss, English, Irish, probably Americans inhabiting Warsaw; where, perhaps, a poor Pole may blunder, and find nothing but the name, to remind him of his oppressed home.

Not far from this, was another small village; the well remembered poetry of beauty that once surrounded it, changed into the sober prose of barrels, boxes, bags, ploughs, &c., marked Moscow; probably just landed from some steamboat. Of such towns, and discharges along the river, there are countless numbers, and unaccountable names.

Davenport, very beautifully situated, near the termination of Rock Island, has, in its prosperity, wholly outstripped the town of Stephenson, on the opposite side of the river. Time or caprice has thus decided in favor of many places, which had, in reality, no superior claims to preference.

Voyaging along the shores of the Mississippi, has afforded an opportunity of comparing them as they lay, in their sequestered pristine beauty in 1836, with their present flourishing state of improvement. All that beautiful heritage of the Sauk Indians in Iowa, over which Black Hawk and his followers roamed, and which was the scene of savage depredation in 1832, is now covered over with farms, under fine cultivation, with comfortable houses, and all the desirable accompaniments of peaceful and abundant living.

Equally sudden are the transitions in

many other places along the river, further
onward.   Equally spirit-stirring is the view
which the future must inevitably unfold.
From Prairie Du Chien to New Orleans, a
distance of more than 2000 miles, an almost
continued village may, in time, stretch along
the Mississippi river, affording outlets for the
productions of the countries in the rear;
while through them, from the south and east,
they will receive their supplies of merchandize.   Luxury, with its seducing train will,
but too soon, move on to the extreme verge
of civilization; and fashion will sit perched
on the heads of the fresh Wisconsin and
Iowa beauties.

Opposite Montrose, a town on the river
near Des Moines, is a settlement of Mor-
mons, refugees to the state of Illinois, amount-
ing, it is said, to nearly three thousand.
Several hundred houses are spread over a
very pretty location, about three miles

square, with land extending back a considerable distance; for which they have not paid
the interest, while they are selling out lots for
money to their followers. In many ways,
their chief men, with their prophet, Jo
Smith at their head, are monopolizing the
property and money of their proselytes.
From accounts given of them by citizens of
Montrose, they are as much to be dreaded
from their marauding propensities, as the
mountain hordes of Scotland that formerly
poured down on their more respectable and
peaceful neighbors.

They call the place Nauvoo, or the New
Jerusalem; and are building a temple sup-
ported by twelve gilt oxen; which is to be
completed by receiving the tithe of each
man's labor. It is an incorporated city, with
judicial tribunal, and a legion of honor, consisting of 800 men, who do military duty·
It must be a ludicrous spectacle, to see Jo

Smith, who is represented as a complete buffoon, figuring as a Mayor, surrounded with his debased Aldermen; or a Mormon Captain, dressed in homespun clothes, drilling his pillaging company of soldiers.

St. Louis, with its interests, has become so intimately associated with a wide extent of the United States; and from its position, such a general thoroughfare for travelling, that little more can be said of it than is already known. As a great Western emporium, its resources are incalculable. It may be called the granary of the fertile west. Its receipt of mineral amounts annually to millions of dollars. The fur trade from the Rocky Mountains, and from St. Peters, at the head of the navigable waters of the Mississippi, serves to swell the lists of its revenue. Immense supplies of merchandize from New Orleans and the eastern cities, the greater part centring here for reshipment, make this the great storehouse for the interchange of the severa lexports from these opposite directions.

St. Louis may trace much of its prosperity to emigration to the West, which in its onward course, may place this city nearly in a central position; thus, perhaps, giving it a claim to the seat of the National Legislation. And the time may be, when the locomotive, in its speed through mountain and prairie, will place it in a vicinity with the Atlantic and Pacific oceans.

This could not have entered into the dreams of the early French settlers, when a beautiful home on this river, shaded by fruit trees, was the boundary of their wishes. This desirable heritage has, almost entirely, passed into the hands of Americans, whose aspirations for wealth and importance seem to acknowledge no limits.

There are, however, a few of the descendants of the primitive settlers remaining, who seem to have a better idea of self-preservation than their ancestors, and who stand unmoved by the changes of time and events. Some of their very pretty country seats in the vicinity of the city, with whole avenues of pear trees, have lately been cut up into city lots; the desire for modern improvements having been grafted on their innate simplicity of taste.

A passing tribute seems due to the Mississippi river, which brings the outpourings of the old and new states to the wharves of St. Louis; at its bidding, fills and empties its warehouses; and on its bosom, bears the traveller to admire its magnificence, and to record its power and rising greatness.

### SLAVERY.

"I would not have a slave to till my ground,
To carry me, to fan me while I sleep
And tremble when I wake."

BEFORE the door of an elegant mansion, belonging to a wealthy planter in Tennessee, a few years ago, stood a negro slave, to ask, in suppliant terms, of his owner, a favor of the deepest interest to himself and family.

A neighboring planter had, at his death, made the following disposition of his slaves. He desired that they should be manumitted and sent to Liberia, when the amount of their labor should be sufficient to defray the expences of transportation; leaving it, however, to their choice to go or remain. That time had arrived. The man who made the petition, had a wife and children among the number destined for removal. A vessel was lying at the wharf at Nashville, ready for their embarkation, when with head uncovered, he thus addressed his master:

"I have come to beg you to buy my wife and youngest child, six months old. She is willing to stay with me and be a slave for life. We have lived together twenty-four years. We will work faithfully, and she will give up her other three children for the sake of living with me. It will make me a better man. It breaks my heart to see her; it kills me." The appeal made to a kind, humane heart was favorably received.

Among the number of slaves, was a brother of the woman—one of those master spirits, ever active, and often influential over the minds of others. This man, working upon her conscientiousness, and representing her future sorrow, when she should be left to realize her separation from her other children; and to reflect that she had assigned herself and her infant to perpetual bondage—by dint of persuasion, added to his urgent reasoning, at length succeeded in hurrying her away, with the others, to the landing. Here ensued a scene of agonized, heart-rending grief. The conflict of her feelings when about to take a last farewell, amounted to frenzy. Amidst her shrieks the brother ejaculating the word freedom! hurried her to the vessel, which was soon under weigh, and out of sight of her bereaved husband.

This family of slaves being for a considerable time at New Orleans, delayed in their embarkation, a part of them fell victims to the yellow fever. The remainder becoming sick at heart, the fair picture of freedom faded away, and they requested to return to Tennessee; where they are at the present time, apparently contented thus to remain.

Many pictures might be drawn of the

comfortable condition of the well fed, well clothed, merry negroes at the south. From a window, at this time, a large, old female slave, dismissed from future toil, is seen walking through the garden, with as much careless, easy independence, as if she were sole proprietor; scolding the white children for picking so many of her "mistess" flowers. Near by, in a cabin door, sits a superannuated man, who appears as if he were calmly waiting a summons to that world where all alike, are free. In striking contrast, about a dozen sleek little blackies are sporting around him; whose descendants may, at some future day, be land-holders or legislators in Liberia.

It is pleasant to hear their songs of rejoicing. on their return voyages of labor on the steam boats, from New Orleans. As they approach their homes, the wooded shores reverberate with the music of "Long Time

Ago;" originating like many others, with these dark improvisatores, falling on the ear in sweet and plaintive cadences.

The assertion may, perhaps, be hazarded, that they are in many instances, at least, as happy as those who have the responsibility of their management. It is too true, that a capricious tyranny sometimes attends the sway held over the slave; yet the amount of labor exacted in his daily task, is by no means equal to the voluntary task of the white man. Severe discipline is often indispensable in keeping in due subordination the propensities and passions of the many, in whose breasts the spirit of a Toussaint or Christophe might be developed, under a relaxation of the accustomed vigilance.

The females at the north need not envy the luxurious leisure of the south. More happiness falls to their lot in the active discharge of domestic duties, than to that of the southern matron, whose cares and vexations, in the midst of wealth, often plant a furrow on her brow.

The active abolitionist has only to have a nearer view of the true situation of things, as they exist in a slave country, to cause him, at least, to divide his sympathies. Still, moral obligation, christian duty, as well as philanthropy bind every man to condemn the principle that favors unequal rights; and to hail the period when a judicious policy may carry into effect, universal emancipation.

The states north of Missouri, own none of these incumbrances. They who wish, or are compelled to rid themselves of them, may there find themselves on an equal footing with others; having always an opportunity of procuring free labor, and imperceptibly gliding into habits of industry that furnish interest for the day and refreshing sleep at night.

## THE POOR.

"And the village bells are on the breeze
    That stirs thy leaf, dark tree!
How can I mourn, amidst things like these,
    For the stormy past with thee?"

"I have come," said a man from a neighboring city, to one who owned a plantation with a hundred slaves, "to ask you for a small corner of your land, to cultivate on shares. My reduced circumstances compel me to resort to labor. My efforts to support my family in town, have not met with sufficient encouragement to warrant my remaining any longer there. With hard work, I trust I can, at least, keep them from present starvation."

Painful is the contemplation of the mass of human wretchedness, at the present time, spread over our republic, falling with an appalling weight on those who, by a reverse of fortune, are hurried from a state of affluence and apparent security, to the depths of penury. When a subject of these vicissitudes comes under our immediate view; where a father is seen looking out for the means of supplying the pressing wants of his wife and children; the sympathy that carries a balm with it, calls for something more effective than mere pity from every individual, who has escaped the withering influences of adversity. To those who, in listless ease, are growing richer, while the poor are growing poorer, from the daily sacrifice of property; the appeal is loud, and should be irresistible, to rise up and contribute to the rescuing of a fellow being from despondence, that too often seizes on the intoxicating bowl, from degradation—alas! that there should be instances of mental alienation, terminating in the horrors of suicide.

To the man already alluded to, as well as

thousands of others, in similar embarrass-
ments, it may be said, "hope on, hope ever;"
as long as a great western domain offers an
asylum, where want need not be known;
where despair need not cloud the mind;
where life may feel a new impulse. New
stimulants are unfolded to active exertion in
all honest occupations; to all classes, whether
men of trade, of art or science. Numerous
water courses present facilities for mills, and
manufactures of various kinds. There are
sources innumerable, from which new smiles
may beam on the face of the disappointed
man.

A benevolent policy would not suffer us
to stop here; while we daily read of the dis-
tresses of the suffering poor, across the Atlantic; shrinking with starvation; and cold
in winter; can we withhold the wish that
they would leave their oppressors, who avert
their eyes from their woes. It would be but

a reciprocation of the sympathies of England, which travel so far to point out evils, existing in greater magnitude at home. Our manufacturing interest, that important branch of industry, judiciously encouraged, might derive advantage from their skill and experience. Our domestic silks and other fabrics might be made to vie with those of foreign importation, and every republican female should be proud to wear them, and would not appear the less interesting that in so doing, she lent her example in aiding the cause of humanity. More patriotic, she certainly would be in extending her influence, which is ever powerful in promoting the public interest. Economy should go hand in hand with industry, in correcting the evils which have grown out of a redundancy of illusory currency. Though our country women have no voice in the councils of the nation, they may, most happily, express their sentiments, by a practical observance of the means which promise to restore prosperity to our country.

As it may be considered that the promise has not been fully redeemed of pointing out the resources of Michigan, Illinois, Wisconsin, Iowa and Missouri, it is perhaps proper here to remark, that the visits of the writer have been generally confined to the two former states; merely passing by portions of the other countries while voyaging past them on the Mississippi river, or having only transient glances of their interior. She has depended more on information from authentic sources than actual observation, and has been thus led to infer, that they have all a general resemblance in point of feature and character, with slight variation of climate. In the absence of mineral, that exhaustless source of wealth, peculiar to some regions,

14

others have perhaps ascendant advantages
which nearly balance.

It is hoped that sufficient inducements
have been pointed out to promote the lively
object of the work; that the picture presented to the view, will be auspiciously received
and contemplated with indulgence; and that
it will be sufficiently attractive to draw a
nearer attention to the great original, which
must ever gain by the comparison. It has
been held out to view, with a motive that has
made the task most pleasing; and an ardent
desire is cherished that it may lead many, by
their star of destiny, to a serene dawning of
happiness, more to be prized, because it promises more endurance than the glare of prosperity, which is often as fleeting as it is dazzling. May many an eye brighten on behold-
ing the blooming freshness of the wide domain; and many a smile light up the faces of
the new residents in *new homes in the west.*

# MUSINGS IN THE WEST.

***

*Many of the following poems have a connexion with the pre-
ceding work, and may almost be considered a continuation of
the subject.*

## TO MY SISTER

O come to the lovely, luxuriant west!
   Come recline with me under my bower;
Where the redbreast sings, and the dove builds her nest,
   In this land of the shade, and the flower.

Come, and wander with me, o'er the beautiful prairie;
   With blossoms all blushing around;
Whose sweets ever charm, and whose hues ever vary,
   As they cluster all over the ground.

The gorgeous fire-lily, and simple wild rose,
   The white, drooping bell of the vale;
Come walk, and "consider" with me, "how it grows,"
   And waves its light stem in the gale.

We will pluck the ripe strawberry, fragrant and glowing,
    And painting our feet as we stray;
While rich, luscious wild fruits, the country o'erflowing,
    Our footsteps will lure, on the way.

How pleased you will be, on the smooth, grassy brink
    Of the lake, so pellucid and clear,
That the deer sees his innocent face when he drinks,
    On its surface, reflected appear.

And the vines bending o'er it, with rich purple cluster,
    With the grand, and the snow-white pond-blossom;
Its broad, green leaves dabbling, and sprinkling their lustre,
    All floating in pride, on its bosom.

I will take you to groves, where the lofty tall oak
    Spreads its dark branches, shadowing o'er us;
Where the delicate fawn, in its light dappled coat,
    Is bounding, in frolic before us.

There, in solitudes deep, and through regions of shade,
    I will point where the hunter, with bow
And feathery arrow, so often has strayed;
    Or where, in his birchen canoe,

He glides o'er the waters, so easy and graceful,
    Nor dreams of the evils in store;
To tear him from his native haunts, now so peaceful,
    The wigwam, the shade and the shore.

View his dark, languid eye, as he's listless reclining,
    Or list to the untutored, plaintive, wild notes

Of the Indian flute, as in distance, it lingers,
　　And swells on the air as it floats.

Leave the world, and its cares all behind—not a sigh
　　Need ruffle the calm of your breast.
Come, come and enjoy all these pleasures with me,
　　In the lovely, luxuriant west!

---

## TO THE REMAINS OF AN ANCIENT FORT, ON ST. JOSEPH RIVER, IN MICHIGAN.

Mysterious mound! what warlike race has thrown
This barrier, here, rude, simple and alone?
How waves the tall, luxuriant grass, o'er those
Who mouldering lie, perhaps, in their repose,
　　　　Beneath the bramble rose,

That sends its balmy odors, on the wind;
In mockery, sporting with the inquiring mind,
Holding its dim lamp, to the misty waste
Of what has floated by, in ages past,
　　　　O'er wildernesses vast.

Doubt, now envelopes thee, in cloud sublime;
Thou mystic relic of the olden Time!

14*

That bears his secrets off, upon his wing;
Pleased dark enigmas, such as these, to fling
                    O'er human wondering.

Wilt thou no ray emit; no light unfold;
Neath the dark curtaining that shrouds the bold?
Comes there no answering sigh, to the opprest
With hope, and fear, and wonder, from the breast.
                    That here, finds rest?

"We've loved around these beauteous wilds to stray;
We've been as you, in ages past away.
Hope, love, and peace have smiled upon our brow—
Ambition, war, revenge have laid us low!
                    More, thou may'st not know."

I go.   Let none disturb this hallowed urn!
To haunts more cheerful, let my footsteps turn—
Flow on, St. Joseph; and in whispers, lave
These shores of beauty, with thy rolling wave,
                    Past the forgotten brave.

## INTEMPERANCE.

I entered a low cottage and beheld,
Alas! a scene that well might touch the heart
Of the most thoughtless.  Sad, desponding, crushed
Beneath the stealthy storms of life, there sat
A female form, surrounded with a group,
That seemed like blossoms on a desert strand.
From her weak hand, I took one tender bud;
And while I looked on its young innocence,
With moistened eye, heard the heart-rending tale
From the pale victim of its father's guilt.

Beyond the Atlantic wave, she said, a home
Had once, been her's; o'er which a sun had shone,
That gilded festive hall and downy couch;
Tinging surrounding objects with the beam—
Withdrawn to shed a death-like gloom.

                          Again,
I saw her; on a wretched pallet, low
She lay, prostrated by disease.  Her cheek
Wore a delusive flush.  Serene her eye.
"O God! thy promises are sweet to me;
Refreshing as the stream that slakes the thirst
Of the worn traveller—Thy will be done."

Two lifeless forms were seen.  The infant gone
Before, to open Heaven's bright portals—Mute,

With all of thought or feeling that is left
In the drained channel; looking on the pale,
Still ruin, stands the author of her woes!

Intemperance! come hither, and behold
Thy withering and blighting influence.
Casting forth, helpless orphans, on the world!
And paralyzing the fresh springs of life;
Exhausting the rich fountain of a heart,
In joy confiding once; only to break.

---

### THE SOUL.

Soul! what art thou, whence, wherefore, and oh! *where?*
A soul would, humbly, of itself, enquire.
What Power directs thy subtle, boundless course;
Grasping the wonders of the natural world—
Embracing, in thy aspirations high,
Systems, both moral and Divine.

　　　　　　Philosophy!
Come near; and of thy gorgeous, mystic folds
Let me disrobe thee: Thou, when unadorned,
Hast beauties, pleasant, to the mental eye;
Yet oft, too oft, thy specious eloquence
Enshrouded in the artificial forms

Of science, to the plain, enquiring mind,
Makes thee repulsive, or at best, emit
A dazzling light.

       Thou tellest me that this power
Its office through the senses, may perform:
The nerves, as agents, serving to convey,
In their mysterious and restless course,
Sensation to the brain; that there the mind
Its seat illustrious holds; and *here* must end;
Sternly forbidden to a higher sphere,
To raise the ardent gaze.

       Can this be so?
A votary of nature would enquire.
Where is the Soul?   The lofty, towering front
Of intellectual man, might seem, in pride,
To answer; and the eloquence of eyes,
Even though the lips are silent, boldly say,
The spirit of Light must hold its empire near—
Within the brain.

       Truly, there, Reason reigns;
And there, her high, august assemblies, holds.
There, memory revels, and luxuriates
On all the past.   The present act may find
Direction; and the future purpose trace
Its origin to this high court, Thought's fair
And beauteous temple, though the heart
Send forth, no embassy, from impulse warm.

In the light, airy chambers of the brain,
Fancy, her bright creations may unfold;
In rich and gorgeous fashioning, array
Beings that only have existence, there;
Flitting on wings of gossamer, with hues
As changeful, as the ever-varying forms,
That float around soft summer's setting sun.
In wild and playful mood, may structures raise
Graceful and light, and towering to the skies—
The soul refusing her fresh, gushing tide
To quench such lightning flashes.

     Who may say,
Even though the cells of thought are rayless, dark,
Reason extinguished, that the breast must cease
To feel, though merry strains, at times, break forth,
From the intenseness of the throbbing brain,
Resembling an inverted pyramid;
Or fitful tones, which the capricious air
Breathes, over wind-harps; or those meteor lights
At evening, flashing transient gleams, behind
Masses of gloomy clouds.

     From spirits wild,
Electric, restless, I oppressed, would turn;
And seek refreshment, in the shadowy bowers
Of nature, in her qeauty and her calm.
The flowers of youthful spring, the rippling rill,
The groves whose leaves are gently quivering

With autumn's low, retiring, farewell sighs;
The rushing torrent and the bounding wave;
On winter's bosom, gems that sparkling glow;
All have their touching and restoring influence.
Who has not felt the magic of the rose,
Baptized in dew, or blushing in the shade?
The indefinable and nameless charm,
Even of an odor, whispering of the past?
How oft has music, borne upon the air,
Swept o'er some chord responsive in the breast;
Making it vibrate to the thrilling note
Of wo, or joy—even though it long had slept.
On the low breathing of the spirit sigh.
As pure, as soft as angels' whispers are,
Is not the language of the soul poured out,
In silent prayer?

        Spring flower and rippling rill;
Autumn's farewell, and mountain wave that bounds;
Bright gems on winter's bosom; thrilling tones
That float upon the air; and prayer fraught sigh;
All, all most eloquently, say, the soul
Its mighty empire, may at least, divide,
Giving the heart a share.

        Religion!
Serene, calm, passionless, thy truth
Looks holy, bidding me to come to thee.
'Tis thou canst teach me, all that I should know,
How bland, and yet how grave the answer comes,

"That subtle power, mysteriously combined
Of thought and feeling, linking earth with Heaven;
Descending from the source of Light and Life,
And Truth; illuminating what were else,
A melancholy ruin, is the Soul:
A jewel, glowing in adversity;
And sparkling brightest, through the humble tear.
The moving spring of all true happiness,
When purpose, elevated and refined,
Shines out, through all the changing scenes of life
To faithless, self-absorbed, and earth-chained man,
Yielding no joys, but such as end in wo.
Know this, and further ask not; when the veil
That now divides us, from that spirit-world, .
Here, only dimly mirrored, on the life
Of patient holiness, shall be removed;
From harps, tinged with rich beams of dazzling light
Streaming from highest Heaven, and swept by wings
Of angels, hymning praises, round the throne
Of Great Jehovah, thou wilt know and feel
*Where is the Soul.*"

## A VOICE FROM IOWA.

Dream of all things thou hast loved,
    As they floated in joy, o'er thy childhood;
Like the breezes of spring, that have moved
    The boughs, in the rich, waving wildwood.

Dream of the rose's soft hue,
    More pale and more fond in its twining;
More fragrant, all sparkling with dew,
    Round columns where moon-light is shining.

Dream of the flower-covered isles,
    Sending sweets, o'er the sea's heaving bosom;
Where the nests of the warbling exiles,
    Rest secure, mid the opening blossom.

Dream of the foam as it dashed,
    And sprinkled the fern, when the fountain,
In sun-light, with splendor has flashed,
    Making greener, the leaves on the mountain.

Ah! some may have dreamed on securely;
    And awoke to the gloom of despair.
May have felt in their waking, too surely,
    How transient all bright visions are!

Come away; and awake from thy dreaming,
    To the side of these deep, crystal rills

O'ershadowed by broad oaks, and gleaming,
　　From valley, dark glen and green hills.

O'er these wild things, the breezes seem lighter,
　　As they breathe of some fairy hand;
And the skies surely shine on them, brighter,
　　Away, in this prairie land.

Not more faithful and true is the feeling,
　　Returned, through the answering eye;
Than bright stars their language revealing
　　In the blue lakes that mirror the sky.

Here, are temples of nature, where even,
　　The leafy, and tall, waving spires
Seem to point the affections to Heaven,
　　And hallow our vows and desires.

In all the bright spells that have bound thee;
　　Creations of fancy-swayed hours;
Nought can equal this flower-world around thee,
　　In the calmness of Iowa's bowers.

A woman in one of the Northern Cities, was imprisoned
for taking three small sticks of wood, on a cold winter night.
In the morning, her children were found at her house frozen
to death.

On drove the stealthy wind;
Fierce raged the storm;
A shivering being braved the blast,
With thin mantle, round her cast.
Thoughts of loved ones, left behind,
Sustained her shrinking form.

Past proud porch, and stately hall,
Swiftly she sped;
Within, the genial fire glows—
Children's merry laugh arose;
Yearning fears, her heart appall—
On, on, she fled♪

Tempted—Alas! she pants for breath;
"If it be harm;
O God forgive!" she seized the wood.
A ruthless watchman near her, stood—
Woman, thy children sleep in death!
*Can he be ever warm?*

Merriment sounds in the festive hall,
Where light and soft the footsteps fall,
On flowers of gorgeous, dazzling dies,

Richly inlaid, under eastern skies.
Couches luxurious, broidered with skill,
Indolent, listless dreamers fill.
Music floats by, with seductive spell;
Witching strains, o'er the senses steal.

Mirrors reflect the joyous glance,
And the buoyant form, in the gliding dance.
Lustrous lamps, shed their mellow ray,
O'er the brow, where rose garlands stray,
Making the wine-cup, look ruby red.
Dainty and rare is the banquet spread.

Ye gay! when your lips, the rich clusters, press,
Think of the lone, and the fatherless;
Brighter than diamonds that sparkle there,
Is the tear that is shed o'er the couch of despair,
Sweeter than perfume from rose-wreath, the voice,
That makes the hungry and cold, rejoice.
Leave, for awhile the bewildering glare;
Come away, to the wretched hovel, where,
Through crevices wide, in the broken wall,
The snow and the sleet, and the night-wind fall.
Meet pillow for wo, is the gentle arm;
Give food, make the shivering being warm—
Calm and light, will your dreamings be;
Ye have gladdened the heart of misery.

## WATER SKETCHES.

Nature! my idol thou hast ever been.
I've loved thee in the breezy morn of life,
Climbing the mountain's brow, o'er rock and glen,
With moss, and brake, and feathery fern o'ergrown,
Listening to water-falls that soothed the ear;
Or gathering cowslips by the rivulet's side.

When gliding, Mississippi! gently o'er
Thy waters bold, from wild St. Anthony,
With Alpine hills and pictured rocks o'erhung;
Laving thy verdant capes and fairy isles;
To those bright sunny shores, where orange groves,
And spicy vines shed perfume all the year,
I've wished all loved ones could be there with me.

Ocean! thy awful beauty I've admired,
Even when on thy bosom, tempest-tost,
That glittered brightest, in its breaking wave;
But most have felt thee, when the starry sky
Reflected, shed a jewelled world, around
The gently gliding bark.

           On Hudson's tide,
Though the appendages of fashion gay,
And outward polish wooed the untutored gaze;
I've waved the dazzling bawbles all aside,

To have a quiet, unobstructed view
Of woodland shore, of cultivated vale,
And highlands bold.

       When Michigan's wide wastes
Have lured me, on my blossom-scented way,
How pleased I've seen the deer, with antlers tall,
Bound lightly o'er the flowers that cluster there,
Or rest securely 'neath his oaken bower.
Or when entranced, delighted, I have stood
On the lone margin of the grass-fringed lakes,
That smile, in limpid calmness; or have viewed
The dusky forest child, in listless ease,
O'er the clear pool, paddle his light canoe,
Say could I love thee less?

       Dipping my wings
In Saratoga's fountains, from the rock
Forever gushing up in sparkling tides—
I've soared aloft, above the things of art,
And coursed my flight across Ontario's sea;
O'er the blue wave, inhaling breezes pure,
Balmy and fresh, from western wilderness—
I've wished such pleasures rich, might be prolonged
On the mind's dreamy waste.

       Niagara!
Nature, in forming thee reserved her powers
Of awful grandeur, majesty and grace;
And in one mighty tide, poured them all forth.

Half frighted, and half pleased at her own work,
She looks out, through her snowy veil of spray,
In all her softly varying, rainbow tints,
And in their blended colors, hovers o'er
Her beauteous task.   In thee, and all her vast
Creations, here, I see a Power Divine,
That, bending low, in reverence, I adore.

———————————

## TO ELIZABETH.

Dost thou know my fair child, with thy tresses so wild,
Profusely, and gaily, adorning
Thy innocent mien, that a power unseen,
Floats around, in the breeze of thy morning?

Of the flowers that lay in your path, every day,
Their colors so softly combining,
That poison oft lies in the varying dies,
Through the wreath, so insidiously twining?

That blisses and woes, like the thorn and the rose,
Are mingled so closely together,
In the wreath you unbind, that you ever will find
They seem as if made for each other?

Hope's enchantment that beams on your bright dawning dreams
More calm and serene will be shining,
When chastened by fears, and sympathy's tears,
O'er your brow, with humility twining.

This page once so white, where affection all bright,
I'ts tender monition has given;
Is not the less fair, for the warm, holy prayer,
That thy hopes may be worthy of Heaven.

---

## THE PILLAR OF CLOUD.

When weary of this changing scene,
    We look into the skies;
We still, may, in that blue serene,
    See evanescent dyes.

May view the clouds near close of day;
    Wild images, there tracing;
Figures grotesque that pass away;
    New forms, their spells effacing.

Spots swimming through the azure way,
    Like birds in the blue ocean;
As fancy lends the plumage gay,
    And aids their gliding motion.

The fairy ship that through the air,
  On melting wave is dancing;
Seems freighted for some haven, where
  Light, on the sail is glancing.

See snowy tents spread out afar,
  Encampments bold surrounding—
By fiery steeds the golden car,
  Through ether, swiftly bounding.

And vast and boundless as the view,
  Wonders on wonders rise;
Earth's things, and earth's illusions too
  Are pictured in the skies.

As human hopes and joys, alas!
  In dazzling visions rise—
Swiftly, the scattered, shapeless mass
  A gilded ruin lies!

Lo! yonder white column, that slowly is rising,
  And curling in beautiful scrolls;
Aspiring aloft, and gracefully poising
  As higher, and higher, it rolls!

The varying hues, of a soft summer even,
  Away to the westward, appear
As if tinged with a light, from the portals of Heaven,
  And a rose tint is resting there,

On that symbol of promise, that once went before
　The faithful of Israel; and I,
Wherever I wander, the source will adore
　Of that column of cloud in the sky.

---

## TO A CHAMPAGNE GLASS OF WATER, FILLED WITH FLOWERS.

Passion flower! why comest thou thus, with a tear *
Thy tendrils so fondly inclining
Towards the first rose of spring; and the daisy so near—
Round its stem thou art almost entwining.

"Straying away, from my wild, sunny home,
From a flower-world gorgeous, and blushing;
To bathe in this cool, limpid wave, I come,
Just dipped from the fount in its gushing."

Crystal cup! flushed with these eloquent things,
In the hand of earth's innocent daughter;
From thee, a lesson of beauty springs;
Sparkling with purest water.

Wine, its oblivious enchantment, may pour,
Its poison insidious, concealing,

*The passion flower always opens with a drop of water.

But the lip may press safely, the brim running o'er,
Pure language of flowers, revealing.

Revellers! unbind quick, the deadly wreath,
From your brows.   Let the wine-cup be broken—
The vine and the rose thus inurned, sweetly breathe
Of temperate pleasures, the token.

----

## THE ALPINE HORN.

At sunset the Shepherds of the Alps, are called together by
a horn, which is the signal for singing a hymn, with the cho-
rus of praised be the Lord.

When the last beams of the setting sun,
   Radiant as angel's wings;
Alps! thy towering breast, shine on,
   The shepherd his offering brings.

Arch! with thy clear and passionless mien,
   Calmly thou seemest to rest
On the highest peaks of the mountain green,
   As the sun goes down in the west.

Sweet to the sound of the shepherd's horn;
   Rising, in mellow accord,

On thee, balmy breeze! are the voices borne,
　　Singing forth, "praised be the Lord."

Hark, 'tis thy clear response, Echo! around,
　　Through grotto and mountain glen, poured,
Lengthening out, the devotional sound,
　　From lowly hearts, praised be the Lord.

Can sanctuary of loftiest dome,
　　Altar more holy, afford,
Nature! than thou, where thy children may come,
　　With their incense of praise to the Lord?

------

### L. E. L.

Ah! is it among the myst'ries of heaven,
That feelings prophetic to high souls are given?
That shadows come o'er the bright dream of our day,
Disenchanting us oft, on our flowery way?—
So thin is the veil they sometimes hold before us,
They throw a sad, mystic influence o'er us.

From the proud castle tower, on the rock-bound coast,
Looked out the bright being that formed its boast,
O'er the bosom wide, of the deep blue ocean;
Imaging there, her own deep emotion,

Who felt beauty alone, in the far off view;
In her restlessness, loved every changeful hue.

The white foam, against the rude cliff, was dashing;
One moment, in sun-lit splendor flashing,
Then gone forever—discoursing alas!
Of hope and joy, that as quickly pass,
In their radiant tints.   The waving palm
Fanned by breezes, forever, freighted with balm,

All, all seemed called up by a fairy hand,
Like the tales she had read of Arabia's land.
Alone, as she gazed on that one star,* nightly,
That kindles and glows, in southern skies, brightly,
Ere it sinks in the wave—herself did she feel
A wandering planet, that soon was to steal

From its path, to a radiant place unknown?
So soon to be missed from the place where it shone.
Alone, the wrapt musings of poesy's daughter,
Broke forth, like the strains of that bird of the water,
That pours o'er the wave, its sweetest, wild lay,
As enchanted, it sings its life away.

Through the clustering flowers, that so lately had shaded
The brow of the bride, should have surely been braided
Dark, cypress leaves.   There, too, should have strayed

---

*The Polar star was, perhaps, the last of her poems.

Some deadly exotic, and enviously played.
The nightshade, insidiously, there should have crept,
And dews in its flower-urn, too, should have wept.

That blushes and smiles, blent with tears and death,
Should find emblems, so soon, in the withering wreath
Encircling the temple, where bright thoughts and high,
Were tinged with a longing for their native sky;
Tinged through the mists of her sad divining,
Ere the mingled sweets were unbound from their twining.

Palm trees, and citron, and myrtle bowers;
Shaken by breezes that scatter your flowers;
Ye speak to the heart, in a sighing tone,
Of a sensitive, tremulous wanderer gone;
Whose life and harp, in unison quivered—
Life and harp, in their melody shivered!

-------

## THE EARLY DEAD.

With flowing scarf, the sable badge of grief,
A train of light and slender forms, went forth;
Whose stifled sighs, that fell upon the air,
Seemed like the breathings of the wind-swayed reed—
Their youthful heads bent low, and tear-wet cheeks,

Like drooping lilies, when surcharged with rain.
These followed, mournfully and slow, the bier
Of one, who late, like them, was flushed with health,
And hope, and love.   How brief the time, since she,
With them, had shared the sport, the fond embrace:
And twined her arm in woodland walk, as gay,
As blithesome in her innocence and joy;
As tuneful birds, that warbled in the boughs
That sheltered them.


Another group was there,
In that sad drapery, whose gloomy folds
Discoursed of broken ties and smitten hearts,
From which, the pall of death shut out the light
That once had beamed there, from the sunny smile
Of youthful joy and love.


Night closed around,
And sleep's light veil, in folds, about me fell;
While sympathy's warm current round my heart,
Was eddying.   The strange, mysterious power
Of dreams came o'er me, and their subtle spell
Brought images of beauty, to my view.
Again, the train of gentle girls appeared—
No sigh, no tear; memory's sweet smile was there.
And they were weaving garlands, fresh and new,
Of buds just broken from the parent stalk
With these they twined with care, the slender stems

Of that frail, sensitive, and timid thing,
That folds its leaves, and shrinks from contact rude,
Expanding only, in the sun's warm ray.
These tokens laid upon a marble shrine,
Breathed out their sweetness o'er the early lost.

Ah! what can chain the spirit's wanderings?
Beyond the clouds, a seraph form appeared,
O'er whose fair brow, a stream of golden light
From Heaven's high throne in brightest radiance fell.
Gems of unearthly lustre, glittered there.
A raptured smile of recognition beamed;
To welcome all the blest, the loved of earth;
To guide their wanderings through ambrosial bowers;
Where the freed soul may rest in calm repose;
And faith and trembling hope are lost in bliss,
In God's own bosom.

Softly swelling strains
As if from harps, touched by some angel power,
So potent o'er the senses, came, they seemed
Steeped in celestial harmonies.   Above,
Around, bright forms of beauty all too light,
Too dazzling for the mortal vision, cast
Their softer shadows.

Ah! 'tis sweet to think,
Agents invisible, around our bed,
On minist'ring errands come, to lead us on,

In our aspirings for that better clime,
Where true joys grow; to be permitted here
Even through the mists of time and death-like sleep,
To have a foretaste of the future world.

Long, were the clear, and spirit tones, prolonged;
Under their strange, sweet influence I woke—
The soul, in calm and pleased bewilderment,
Lingering on the confines of earth and Heaven.

---

## TO THE BRIDE.

This morning, a young, timid thing
Within my window flew;
The rustling of whose new-fledged wing,
My pleased and curious wondering
                  Quickly drew.

The voluntary prisoner,
Within a vase, that flushed
With summer's richest, gayest flowers,
Gathered but lately, from the bowers,
                  Where they had blushed.

Soon found itself entangled there,
Within the clustering mesh;

**16\***

Fearless of lurking danger, where
All seemed so simple, and so fair,
> Balmy and fresh.

I fear to handle thee too rude,
My trembling, gentle guest;
Say, what allured thee, to intrude
Upon my musing solitude?
> Come to my breast.

Thou dost, ah! little twittering thing,
A mystic language hold,
If here thou comest on angel wing,
Tidings of peace and joy to bring,
> Wilt thou unfold?

Dark presage could not come from seer
All light and gay like thee;
The mission thou art sent to bear,
Tell, and I'll send thee through the air,
> In joyous liberty.

Say, hast thou left the sheltering side
Of a fond, fostering mother;
Thy peace, securely to confide,
Like to a young and timid bride,
> With another?

Thou, with white flowers in thy hair,
Come hither, view with me,

The emancipation through the air,
Of one so gentle bright and fair,
                    *Emblem of thee!

———  ———————————


## TO EUGENIA.

Come to me my lyre! in the cypress boughs, thou hast hung,
In shadowy gloom enshrouded, all neglected and unstrung;
A lip resistless, bids me touch thy trembling strings once more,
That long have slept in silent night, along the surge-wet shore.
Bring roses filled with dewdrops, from yonder clustering vine;
And let me with these darker leaves, their brighter beauties
          twine;
It should be full of joyousness; something light and free,
                    That is for thee.

O! that the chords that vibrate now, so thrillingly to me,
And almost fright me back, from the task set by thee;
Awaking thoughts responsive, so all unlike the lay
That should so gaily sweep the strings, on this thy natal day,
Could, in their numbers, pour along, some magic melody,
At once to still the rising sigh, and wake to extacy,
                    Thy heart of glee.

*She soon passed away.

But ah! remember, in the dawn of thy life's breezy day,
Though thy rising sun be cloudless, and every object lay,
In thy early pathway, tinged with the brightness of its ray;
The radiant beam is never lent, on aught, around you, laid,
But *beside the gilded favorite, there ever rests a shade*—
And often, checkered is the bower, in which you would recline,
Like that destiny of thine.


There are flowers, that only open when the sunbeam is with-
    drawn,
Reserving all their odors for the pale, cold moon;
That will only shed their incense on the still night air—
The leaflet wet with dew, in its influence is most rare,
And adverse gale will farthest bear its breathing from the vine,
On that brow of thine.


The rill that murmurs past thee, so serenely clear to-day,
Is not always, unimpeded, on its smooth and grassy way;
But often, over rocks, and through the mountain glen must
    roam,
And struggle in its restlessness; impatient for a home,
Through fern and feathery brake: till its waves again subside,
And the sky is seen reflected, on its crystalline tide.
Thus, is Heaven, in its calmness, imaged on the life divine;
And may such be thine.


Thou knowest, the clouds of evening that thou lovest to look
    upon,

Are more touching and serene, when their glory is withdrawn;
Ever varying in their form, ever changeful, in their hue,
Till their soft and fleecy outline faintly melts from the view;
So pure, and so etherial, may thy chainless spirit soar,
                    When thy life is o'er.

---

## NIAGARA.

In nature's darkest, gloomiest mood,
She formed this rugged scene!
Then stood aloft, and viewed the flood,
With wild and troubled mien—
She smoothed her brow, and sweetly smiled;
Viewing her wonders o'er;
And while amid the flowing sheet,
The rainbow played about her feet,
Dashing the spray off from her locks,
She gaily cried,
I'll sport this way no more!

## STORM AT NIGHT.

O welcome wild Erie! the roar of thy ocean;
   There's music and wail in the swell
Of thy bosom, that heaves with a lofty emotion;
   And sighs out a deep-toned farewell.

To summer, its fragrance from blossoming roses;
   Its light notes of joy from the spray,
Which the robin has left, and with mirth, now reposes,
   Unconscious of change, in the south's sunny ray.

Gay minstrels, what love, and what sweets there, await you,
   From bowers of the orange and lime;
Where soft, wooing gales, in their fondness will meet you,
   And welcome you back to the clime.

Where the vine in its clustering profusion is swinging,
   And flaunting in pride o'er the wave;
Its spicy perfumery, in dalliance flinging,
   And bending, its beauties to lave.

Farewell too, in sadness, to bright summer morning;
   The radiant sun of mid-day.
To the gorgeous drapery, the evening adorning,
   As its glory is fading away.

In unison ye, with the bosom of gladness,
   With all that is peaceful and fair;

Ye illy chime in, with the stricken heart's sadness,
    That finds a response to its care.

In the music, O Erie! that pours from the shell
Of thy caverns so dreary, and sighs out farewell—
What spirit of darkness, is lodged in the cloud,
That o'er thee is hovering, so angry and loud?

        Now subdued, lowly sighing,
        Like piteous wail;
        Now like moans for the dying,
        Poured out on the gale.

        Ah! welcome the rude blasts,
        Ah! welcome the knell;
        They are echo'd by sad gusts,
        That breathe out farewell.

        To the raptures of life,
        To the bright dream of day;
        As they, in the strife
        Of the storm, flit away.

Through the swift flying clouds for a moment how clear
The moon—through a shroud, can more holy appear
The beaming of hope?   Lo! a speck meets the view,
A dark, floating wreck, of what once was new,
And buoyant and graceful; soft wafted by gales
Propitious and peaceful, it spread its light sails—

See the lone ruin ride
On the rude mountain wave,
That covers the grave
Of glory and pride!

The morn appeared, the sun, in glory rose,
And all, around, was hushed in calm repose.
The storm-cloud hovered o'er the wave, no more:
Light, feathery surges played along the shore,
Reflecting on their crests, more jewelry
Than ever glowed on brow of royalty.

A voice came o'er the low, subsiding swell
And softly murmured, "say no more farewell,"
Does not the air emit a sweeter balm?
And to the storm, succeed a soothing calm?
When waking from its wintry, chill repose,
Will not, with deeper glow, blush forth the rose?
With richer hue, will not the woodland glen,
And hill and valley, smile on you again?

The rill may image forth the sleep of death,
But often, ripples, on its way, beneath
Its white and icy covering; 'neath the ray
Of vernal sun, will it not melt away,
And dance o'er pebbly bed, more joyously,
Than frolic wild, of buoyant infancy?
More welcome, renovated buds appear,
Than plains, where pomgranates thoughout the year,
Spread their unchanging blush, loth to retire;

Leaving no room for hope, or fond desire.
The sighing of the waves will soon be o'er,
And they will flow as softly as before;
Mirroring all the beauties of the sky,
From dawn, and noon, and evening radiancy.
Though songsters, now have voyaged south to tell
Their raptures fond, they utter no farewell.
Returning from their pilgrimage of air,
Will not their plumage still, as gay appear,
As varying, in their flower-imparted hue,
As in their warbling strains, forever new?
To catch their wild and thrilling melody,
Must you not raise your vision to the sky?
Connecting links, between this earth and heaven,
To cheer and elevate, are kindly given.

Chain not your thoughts to earth, but raise them higher,
Look up, and, to the spirit-world aspire.
Hope's brightest tints are pictured in the sky;
All, all that's best and purest is on high.

----

## TO AUGUSTA.

As o'er the deep blue lake I glide,
And tears fall fast and free;
Ling'ring along the vessel's side,

**17**

The melting shores to see,
      I'll think of thee.

Chiding the fresh up-springing gale,
That bears me swiftly on;
Filling the proudly swelling sail;
A sigh on it for pleasures gone,
      I'll send to thee.

And when o'er western wilds I stray,
With clustering flowers before me;
On my enchanted, perfumed way,
Memory's bright plume wide o'er me,
      I'll think of thee.

In prairie lands I've often thought,
The skies were clearer, brighter;
That breezes, swept o'er wild things, brought
An influence balmier, lighter,
      Purer, to me,

Alone, where nature through deep glen,
Revels by dancing rills;
That laugh, and sparkle brighter, when
They tell of the green hills
      They've left to me.

And when I weave the garland fair,
I'll think how every blossom
Would grace thy simply parted hair,
And softly shade the bosom
      Of one like thee.

For blessings rare on all that's mine,
I'll breathe on it a prayer;
And bending at some lowly shrine,
I'll leave the offering there,
  For them, and thee.

In that soft, touching, sun-set hour
Sacred to lonely musing;
When rosy clouds their mellow power
Are o'er the heart diffusing,
  Then wilt thou think of me?

When sombre clouds, with edge of gold,
In masses float before thee,
The affections—and the hopes behold,
That Heaven will yet restore me,
  Once more, to thee.

At morning, when my own loved flower
The rose—and mignonette
Are clustering, wildly, in thy bower,
Thou can'st not then forget
  To think of me.

When in the vase they gaily blush,
Their varied hues combining;
Think how I loved, in their rich flush,
To trace fond sisters twining;
  Not torn away like me.

*One hour*—the holy sabbath hour,
When music wakes the feeling—
The organ's peal—and prayer's high power—
When thoughts from earth are stealing;
   Then I will think of thee.
 *Steamer, on Lake Erie.*

———————

## ASPIRATION.

In solitudes where languid listlessness,
And dreamy musings of uncertain things,
Serve, with their subtle, and mysterious sway,
Only to paralyze the springs of life;
To chill the pulse, where warm philanthropy
Should freely flow; will only dim the eye,
Which never beams so quietly serene,
As when reflecting the bright consciousness
Of those diviner charities that bless,
Twice bless, the minist'ring and the relieved,
We may not always roam, and heedless, waste
Life's fleeting moments.

    Deep sequestered shades!
Henceforth adieu. I may not love you more;
Or only love you, when from you, I learn

Lessons of usefulness.   Ye sheltering trees,
And bowers of fragrance, I may turn to you
Only to read a language written here.
Whirlwinds may twist yon pines, your towering fronts
Tall oaks! with adverse gales may bend; at night,
Your trembling leaves, in heavy rains, be drenched;
Yet in the calm and sunny morn, is not
Your light and buoyant gracefulness restored?
And for the fresh libation o'er you poured;
Do you not wave in gratitude profound;
Your joy acknowledging for sun and shower,
By stretching out your kindly arms of shade?

Methinks your woven screenery says to me,
In gentle whispers, I must walk abroad;
Nor turn aside from social communing,
Save when oppressed with earthly thrall, I yield
For a brief moment, to the influence
Cheering and bland, of what I e're must love,
And may, the timid, shrinking violet,
And Feeling's emblem, the dew-sprinkled rose—
Ah! e'en from this creation of fair things,
Does eloquence most sweet, sink in the heart.
The gentle winds of Heaven that o'er them move,
The low, mysterious mission seem to bear.
"We live, to scatter wide, our essences;
Send honeyed dews, on the industrious wing;
Shelter the tender lambkin, 'neath our robes
Of blossoming hedge; and charitably screen

The panting deer that flies from hunter's shaft.
O'er wounded dove that comes on drooping wing
Our lilies bend in tearful sympathy—
Oft in the deep and chilly hour of night,
We give out odors to the brow of care;—
O'er the asylum of the exile lone,
From clustering vines, pour out, our richest balm.''